MINISTRY OF
AGRICULTURE, FISHERIE[S]

British Poisonous Plants

A. A. FORSYTH, M.R.C.V.S., D.V.S.M.

Sometime Principal and Professor of Veterinary Surgery
in the Glasgow Veterinary College

Bulletin 161

LONDON
HER MAJESTY'S STATIONERY OFFICE

First published 1954
Second edition 1968
4th Impression 1976

ISBN 0 11 240461 8

Foreword

In the years which have passed since the first publication of this Bulletin in 1954, there have been substantial advances in our knowledge, and botanical books and classification have undergone revision.

The present edition represents an up-to-date and scrupulous assessment of our present knowledge in this field. In particular, new knowledge of the effects of moulds and their toxins and increased information on classical and well-known causes of poisoning such as ragwort, ergot, kale, bracken and buttercups have permitted expansion of the relevant sections.

The Bulletin, as before, is written in non-technical language and provides a valuable source of information in a field requiring the contribution of several diverse disciplines.

Ministry of Agriculture, Fisheries and Food.

H. I. Field
Director Central Veterinary Laboratory

July 1967

(132217) A2

Author's Preface

In writing *British Poisonous Plants*, I have borne in mind that human poisoning by growing plants is as unusual in Britain as plant poisoning of the domestic animals is commonplace. Although losses of livestock from plant poisoning may be considerable, they are in reality very small when compared with the enormous losses from this cause sustained by many of the more recently developed countries. British agriculture has been a model for the world for many centuries, and tradition and folk-lore, as well as the development of scientific methods, have played their part in ridding a large part of the country of such noxious weeds as corn cockle and darnel, and of parasitic fungi like ergot. Thus, the chances are remote of poisoning by them ever reaching epidemic proportions, as sometimes happens in other parts of the world.

The only people fully equipped for the treatment of plant poisoning in man and animals are the doctor and the veterinary surgeon respectively, and whenever there is the slightest suspicion of poisoning there should be no delay in summoning their aid. Most of the fatal cases begin with the mildest of symptoms, and the chances of recovery lessen as the hours go by. Wherever practicable in the text, first-aid treatment is suggested, with simple remedies which are to be found in almost every house and which will not interfere with any medical or veterinary treatment likely to be prescribed later. It must be fully understood, however, that none of these remedies can possibly take the place of professional treatment.

The book is written primarily for the stockowner and country reader in as simple language as possible, but as technicalities have inevitably crept in, a glossary has been appended to help in the better understanding of them. Readers who are in doubt or difficulty over the identity of plants should consult a Flora, and for this purpose I recommend *Flora of the British Isles*, 2nd edition, 1962, A. R. Clapham, T. G. Tutin and E. F. Warburg (Cambridge University Press) and *The Concise British Flora in Colour*, 1965, W. Keble Martin (Ebury Press & Michael Joseph).

For research workers and those who wish to read further on any poisonous plant or poison, a selection of suitable references is given at the end of each botanical family. Some are in foreign languages but most of them have a summary in English, French, or German, and, in a few instances this is indicated. Most of the references given are to work published subsequent to 1935.

In the one and a half decades which have elapsed since I prepared the manuscript for the first edition of *British Poisonous Plants*, the emphasis in plant toxicology in Britain has shifted very markedly from wild-growing species to cultivated fodder plants. There are many reasons for this, not the least being the wholesale disruption of those two great reservoirs of wild plant life, hedge-banks and roadside verges. In addition, present day intensification, increased mechanization and advances in storage techniques, together with the greater reliance placed upon a single forage crop rather than on the wider mixtures of former times, have all played their part. And who can say whether 'blooms' of toxic algae, types of which are known to occur in Britain, may, with wider adoption of the lagoon system of farm effluent disposal, prove to be a future potential hazard?

The most significant advances have been in the field of biochemistry. New and improved laboratory techniques for the isolation and identification of toxic substances and for assessment of their effects upon the animal body, have produced findings of the highest importance which include mycotoxins in imported groundnuts and cotton seed, goitrogens in crucifers and other plants and carcinogens in aflatoxin and in bracken.

Over the same period, a great deal has been written in the world's professional and scientific literature on the subject of plant poisoning, much of it merely confirming or reiterating what was already well known and accepted. Consequently, I have refrained from referring to articles which have not added to existing knowledge.

I would like to express my gratitude to those of my friends and professional colleagues, too numerous to mention individually, who, from all parts of the country, have provided me with material and information. The relevant departments of the Ministry of Agriculture, Fisheries and Food have once more placed their vast resources of material and library facilities at my disposal and their officers have given unstinted aid. My especial thanks are due to Sir George Taylor, D.SC., F.R.S.E., F.L.S., V.M.H., Director of the Royal Botanic Gardens, Kew, and to his colleague Mr. C. C. Townsend, F.L.S., who checked the botanical details and made many helpful suggestions; to Dr. A. B. Paterson, PH.D., B.SC., M.R.C.V.S., D.V.S.M., F.R.I.C., Deputy Director and Dr. Ruth Allcroft, O.B.E., D.SC., PH.D., B.SC., Senior Research Officer of the Central Veterinary Laboratory, Weybridge and Mr. R. M. Mack, M.R.C.V.S., Assistant Director of the Commonwealth Bureau of Animal Health, whose interest and many contributions at all stages have been of inestimable value, to Mr. H. A. Forsyth, B.SC., N.D.A., M.INST.BIOL., who has read the manuscript from the viewpoint of an independent agriculturalist and has given very considerable assistance and advice; and last, but by no means least, to Mr. H. I. Field, M.SC., F.C.PATH., M.R.C.V.S., Director of the Central Veterinary Laboratory, for having written the Foreword.

A. A. FORSYTH

Acknowledgment of Illustrations

The illustrations comprising Plates I, II, III, IV, V, VI and VIII were reproduced from photographs supplied by Messrs. Flatters and Garnett Ltd., and Plate VII was reproduced from a photograph supplied by the author.

Contents

About Poisonous Plants

In introducing the subject of poisonous plants and plant poisoning, it is first necessary to define what is meant by the term 'a poisonous plant'. Broadly speaking, a poisonous plant is one which gives rise to a serious departure from normal health when a small quantity of its fruit, root or vegetation is eaten by a creature which is susceptible to its effects. This definition covers the majority of the plants to be described later, but there may be some readers who will consider that it is not broad enough, and others that it covers too wide a field. It will, however, serve our purpose in attempting to pick out some of the most dangerous species from the many hundreds of plants which are natives of Great Britain. A few of the commoner cultivated plants and shrubs of exotic origin, but definitely known to be dangerous, have been included, but if one attempted to write on the possibilities of poisoning by the great number of species which are cultivated in British gardens the task would be Herculean, and totally outside the scope of this work.

PLANT NAMES

The English names of plants given in this book are those which are most commonly used throughout Great Britain, but it is recognized that many plants are known by other names in different localities and it has not been possible to include them all.

It is as useless to talk of 'ben weed' in London as it is to refer to 'ragwort' in some parts of the West of Scotland, although one is referring to the same plant. To avoid misunderstanding arising from the use of these local names, botanists have named and classified all known plants. First, they are broadly divided into families, and the family again divided into genera. Each genus is divided into species, which may again be subdivided into varieties.

Every plant is given a name which consists of two Latin words, and most of them are descriptive. The first is the generic or 'surname' and the second is the species, specific, or 'christian' name. These two are followed by the abbreviated name of the author or authors who were first responsible for describing the species under that particular name or combination. When a subsequent author or authors decide that the plant really belongs to a different genus or should have a different rank from that in which it was originally described, the name of the author who first described a species is given in brackets, the transferring author's name follows outside the brackets.

When two different botanical names are given for the same plant the first is the one which is generally accepted as correct at the present time. The abbreviation 'syn.' for synonym, is followed by the name by which the plant was formerly known.

The majority of plant names given in this publication are as listed in *Flora of the British Isles*, 2nd edition (1962), by Clapham, Tutin and Warburg.

SUSCEPTIBILITY TO POISONOUS PLANTS

There is a wide difference between man and each of the various domesticated animals, in their susceptibility to the effects of plant poisons. The difference is dependent upon the internal arrangement of their respective digestive systems and the juices they elaborate. A cow, for instance, with its great churning rumen, can safely eat quantities of the more irritant plants which would kill a horse or a pig; and the digestive juices of a rabbit are able to neutralize the poison of the Death Cap Mushroom (*Amanita phalloides*) in amounts sufficient to kill a whole human family.

FOOD PLANTS WHICH ARE POISONOUS

Many of our commonest food plants may become lethal under certain conditions of growth or preparation. The oat, believed to be the safest of all food plants for man and beast, when grown on certain American soils stores saltpetre (potassium nitrate) in its stems and leaves in sufficient quantities to kill animals which eat even small amounts of the straw or oat hay, while the grain remains quite wholesome. Wheat, from which bread is made, and barley, from which beer is brewed, if fed to the horse whole or ground into meal, cause severe illness, and if he recovers from the acute stages he may, and often does, remain lame for the rest of his life. The humble potato—mainstay of human diet—if exposed to light long enough to become green, elaborates a poison which will kill man or animals if sufficient is eaten; and the author has, on several occasions, made post-mortem examinations of pigs which have died after eating quantities of growing tomato plants. Mustard, a common enough salad crop, if allowed to grow to maturity and form pods, may kill sheep fed on it, particularly if frosted. Reports of deaths among pigs which have been fed on boiled turnips, swedes, and beetroot are common from all parts of the world. The list can be continued *ad infinitum*.

Custom, and the traditional methods of preparation and of feeding, have prevented severe losses from any of these substances. It is not customary to feed horses on wheat or barley; if they eat it, they do so only by mistake. The housewife discards green potatoes because they cook badly and are unpleasant to eat. The fruit of the tomato is not poisonous; the poisonous substance is only in the stem and leaves and they are not eaten. The taste of mustard becomes far too 'strong' for the human palate long before it is poisonous, and farmers, following tradition, feed their sheep on it before the pods are formed. Turnips, swedes, and beetroot, cooked normally and eaten fresh, are perfectly harmless, the trouble arises only after they have been kept for a long time in the water in which they were boiled.

INDIVIDUAL REACTIONS AND ALLERGIES

Individuals, both men and animals, vary in their reactions to many of our everyday fruits and vegetables and, in this connection, the old adage that 'One man's meat is another's poison' can never be refuted. The author himself cannot eat raw apples or drink cider without an immediate skin reaction, and one of his friends suffers acute abdominal pain if he eats a single plum. Another appears to be suffering from measles a few minutes after eating a single strawberry. These individuals know their idiosyncrasies and avoid taking any foods likely to contain their own special poison.

It is very difficult, in both human and veterinary medicine, to pin these reactions or 'allergies' down to one or other fruit or plant during their first or second occurrence, particularly as they have seldom been eaten alone. The same applies to pollens; many skin tests may have to be applied before the offending one can be identified, as every sufferer from hay fever knows only too well.

WHY EVERYONE DOES NOT DIE OF POISONING

The foxglove is recognized as the most universally poisonous plant. Everyone knows that those persons or animals that eat it will die, and there are few places in Britain, fields, woodlands and gardens, where it cannot be found growing in profusion. Yet the British literature of the past twenty years contains only one reported incidence of poisoning—of young turkeys. Why then, with this harbinger of death all around us, do not more children or animals die from its effects? The answer is very simple; it has a nasty taste, and even if animals or children take a little into their mouths they spit it out again quickly, without swallowing, long before it has time to do any harm. The foxglove is not alone in this respect; most of the plants which are known to contain the deadliest of poisons also have an unpleasant taste or odour, and because of it they are avoided by human beings and animals alike. This is the real reason why the incidence of death and severe illness from plant poisoning is so low, even in conditions where the potentialities for poisoning are apparently unlimited.

ADDICTION AND CRAVING FOR POISONOUS PLANTS

Children and animals will sometimes eat noxious things with apparent relish and disastrous effect. Why they do so is a mystery, and the times when their appetites are likely to become depraved are as unpredictable as the British weather. The question may perhaps be more sympathetically approached when one remembers that the taste of the first glass of beer, the first cigar, or the first pipeful of tobacco is not pleasant. It may give rise to such nausea that the tyro remains a teetotaller or non-smoker for the rest of his life. On the other hand, another member of the same family, who is just as nauseated, may develop a craving, which is apparently insatiable, for one or more of these things.

It is said that animals never become drug addicts, but this is hardly true. Once an animal acquires the taste for anything, good or bad, it will go to endless trouble to satisfy its craving. Most country veterinary surgeons and many stockowners can recall cases of animals which, having recovered from acute poisoning, have returned at the first opportunity to gorge again on the offending plants, often with more dire results than before. During early convalescence many animals will flatly refuse to eat normal foodstuffs, although they will hungrily devour the plant which poisoned them. In these instances, where the plant has not been identified, they will often lead one directly to it, if turned out again into the same pasture.

From among the many plants for which horses and cattle may develop a craving, particular mention may be made of: buttercups, bryony, horse-radish, woody nightshade, laurel, rhododendron, acorns, oak leaves, ash leaves, and rushes.

POISONING BY TREES AND SHRUBS

Of our trees and shrubs, the most deadly is the yew. Cattle which eat it are often found lying dead under the tree with twigs and leaves still in their mouths. Because their toxicity was so well known, yew trees, for the production of bow staves, were planted from the earliest times in churchyards and gardens; places to which animals could not normally gain access.

For this reason the number of cattle affected by yew poisoning is very much lower than those which suffer the ill-effects of eating fallen acorns and oak leaves or the 'keys' and leaves of the ash. Sheep are seldom or never affected by these trees; they are more selective in their grazing than horses or cattle, they do not pick up many leaves or acorns, and they are not tall enough to reach the green branches. Pigs thrive on acorns in the autumn and are often turned into pastures where they abound, to eat them as they fall, and thus prevent cattle from being poisoned by them.

POISONING BY EVERGREENS

Evergreen poisoning is more commonly seen during the winter months, when, after heavy falls of snow which cover the pastures, the hungry creatures will eat anything which is green, and are likely to break into woodlands and shrubberies for shelter.

POISONING BY PLANT ROOTS

During such normal winter farming operations as excavations for the laying of pipes and drains, or the cleaning out of ditches and watercourses, poisonous roots, like those of laburnum, the bryonies and water dropwort, may be unearthed and, through carelessness or ignorance of their character, may be left lying on the surface, an open invitation for animals to gnaw or eat them.

After any work of this description has been completed, all roots left lying about should be collected, taken to a safe place and burned. Neglect of this simple precaution has led to many losses among livestock, both in this and in other countries.

The owner of the cattle poisoned with white bryony (described on page 72) disregarded the author's advice to burn the remaining roots. Instead he collected them together and buried them to 'rot down' in a heap of stable manure where, during the summer, they produced a luxuriant crop of bryony.

VARIATIONS IN THE POISONOUS PROPERTIES OF PLANTS

The quantity of the poisonous substances contained within the plant depends very much upon its strain and the conditions under which it it grown; soil, climate, altitude and season, all have their effect. Thus a plans grown in the Highlands of Scotland may contain much more poison than another of the same species grown on the Romney Marsh, or vice versa.

The poisons are not always evenly distributed throughout the whole plant. In one the roots may contain most, in another the stem and leaves, while in yet another it is mostly in the fruits.

The stage of growth is important too; some plants are poisonous at all times; others show no signs of it until the flowers are formed.

Some of the poisonous substances are not stable compounds and may break down into non-poisonous ones on drying and storing. Proto-anemonin, the poison of buttercups, is of this type. A quantity of buttercups, which would kill an animal if eaten in the green state, is perfectly harmless when made into hay. This is not always the case, however, for many plant poisons remain stable after long periods of drying and storage, and a large number withstand boiling. Foxglove, horsetail, and ragwort, are a few examples of plants which are as poisonous if eaten in hay as they are in the fresh, green state.

POISONOUS PLANTS EATEN IN MISTAKE FOR OTHERS

Occasionally poisonous plants are eaten by man, or are given to animals, in mistake for others. The root of monkshood has, in more than one instance, been eaten in mistake for horse-radish and caused the death of the people who ate it. Bulbous buttercup roots have caused distressing symptoms of illness in children who sometimes mistake them for pignuts, and the author has strong recollections of investigating the death of a litter of young pigs to which evacuee children had given the 'red currants' they had picked from a *Daphne mezereum* bush, fortunately without having swallowed any themselves. Almost every year a few cases of 'mushroom' poisoning are recorded after poisonous fungi have been mistaken for edible varieties.

POISONOUS PLANTS IN MEDICINE

From the earliest times, many of the poisonous plants have been used in the preparation of medicines. They are still cultivated and gathered in much the same way but, instead of being brewed or stewed over the kitchen fire, they are now extracted and prepared in the laboratory, where they are chemically and biologically assayed and brought to a high standard of therapeutic efficacy.

The popular fallacy that the lore and knowledge of the properties of plants in medicine has been lost, is totally without foundation. There never was a period in the world's history when more was known of their actions and uses than today, and there never was a time when more of them were used. This belief has in part come about through the elegance of their preparation by the modern pharmacist who, instead of preparing the vile and malodorous potions of the past, presents the same substance in the form of a white tablet, similar in appearance to every other white tablet.

The knowledge of plants and their poisons is no longer the stock-in-trade of the wise-woman and the charlatan, but is in the safe keeping of the expert pharmacist and pharmacologist, who apply it solely for the benefit of mankind, not as in the distant past when it was chiefly used to cause acute discomfiture or sudden demise.

The Plant Poisons

PLANTS exert their poisonous effects by substances which they elaborate during growth. Some of these substances are as yet unknown or, if known, little is understood of their action on the body. The great majority, however, are well known and in many instances they are extracted and used medicinally.

VOLATILE OILS AND ACRID SUBSTANCES

Volatile oils and acrid substances are present in many plants, often in addition to other poisons. They exert their effects by irritation and, in some cases, by coagulating the proteins of the stomach and bowel walls. They may be absorbed into the blood-stream and cause damage to any part of the body as they circulate, and may be excreted in the sweat, the saliva, the breath, the milk and the urine.

These substances are the common cause of the tainting of milk and flesh. Animals often refuse to eat plants which contain large amounts of volatile oils because of the unpleasant odour and obnoxious or burning taste. Examples are: the volatile oil of mustard, and tannic acid or tannin, which is present in acorns and bracken.

GLYCOSIDES

The poisonous glycosides are complex chemical substances which break down on fermentation, or by interaction with dilute mineral acids, to yield sugar, and other compounds which are poisonous. Most plants which contain glycosides also contain the ferments or enzymes which will break them down, and when these are brought into contact, either inside or outside the body, they cause their poisonous effects.

The most dangerous of them yield prussic acid (hydrocyanic acid—HCN), and are known as cyanogenetic glycosides. They are found in apricot, cherry, peach and plum kernels, in apple and pear pips, in cherry laurel, linseed, millet, sorghums, wild white clover, some of the rushes and many other plants.

The acute symptoms of prussic acid poisoning are well known for there are few, if any, other poisons which, if taken by the mouth, will cause death so quickly. The animal breathes rapidly for a few seconds, then falls on its side and dies, usually after howling or bleating and a short-lived, spasmodic struggle.

Man, unless deliberately poisoned with proportionately large doses, is apparently less susceptible to its effects than most animals, particularly the dog and pig. Much of the rapidity of its action depends upon the acidity of the stomach at the time of ingestion. Foods containing these glycosides are seldom eaten alone in quantity by man. Sugar has a definite effect in preventing its action, and it is believed that sugar in the wine, to which prussic acid had been added, actually saved Rasputin when an attempt was made on his life in 1916.

Any attempt to save the life of a human being or animal suffering from prussic acid poisoning must be made immediately; sugar, and hyposulphite of soda (photographer's 'hypo') in a 5 per cent solution, are the antidotes most likely to be obtainable in emergency. Ammonia, and ammonium carbonate well diluted with water are also very helpful in these cases. If one or other cannot be given by the mouth, their ammoniacal fumes may be inhaled and artificial respiration applied. Intravenous injections of methylene blue are recommended for use in both man and animals, but such treatment is beyond the scope of first-aid.

Chronic prussic acid poisoning is not so easily recognized as the acute form. Human beings and animals that take small quantities of it suffer from a condition in which the tissues are unable to take up oxygen from the blood, which remains a bright red; in many cases it is even bright red in the veins. Thus the tissues become oxygen-starved and other products appear in the blood.

The rumen of cattle, sheep and goats is capable of neutralizing much larger quantities of prussic acid than the simple stomach of non-ruminants but, in doing so, thiocyanate, a goitrogen or substance able to cause goitre or severe thyroid dysfunction, may be formed. From this it may be inferred that any plant which contains a cyanogenetic glycoside can be a potential cause of goitre should sufficient of it be eaten over a period.

Plants of widely differing families produce goitrogens of which probably the first to be recognized was thiouracil, which was found in descendents of wild cabbage (*Brassica oleracea* L.). The worst offenders of this species are the three main varieties of kale which, by their very nature and the large quantities in which they are fed, rather than by greater goitrogen content, are far more dangerous to livestock than the others.

Both thiocyanate and thiouracil are absorbed into the blood-stream from the alimentary tract and act by binding the natural iodine of the body to protein, thus rendering it unavailable for use by the thyroid, the general effect being indistinguishable from true iodine deficiency.

The feeding to pregnant cows and ewes of kale, linseed, linseed cake meal, cyanogenetic strains of white Dutch clover and other plants containing cyanogenetic glycosides has occasioned considerable loss of progeny and disastrous interference with breeding programmes here in Britain and in many other parts of the world. The effect has been death of the foetus or arrest or alteration of its development, particularly of its thyroids. Non-infectious abortions and full term still-births have been common sequelae, depending very much upon the stage of foetal development at the time when such feeding commenced. Living calves and lambs from affected mothers have shown signs of goitre with enlarged thyroids, but many of these, if not too badly affected, have made good recovery after receiving appropriate iodine therapy.

Fortunately, the provision of supplementary iodine during feeding with goitrogenic fodder plants can be of great value but, to be fully effective, the amount given must, of necessity, be in excess of that which the goitrogens can bind to protein.

Except for its effects, goitre of goitrogenic plant origin is in no way connected with that produced by genetic factors nor by life in hard water districts, where there is deficiency of iodine in soil and water. The disease can occur anywhere and plants from which goitrogens are derived need not, of necessity, be grown upon iodine deficient soil.

Goitrogens circulate in the blood-stream and are excreted in the milk of lactating animals while being fed upon goitrogenic fodder plants and it is a matter for speculation as to how many calves and young children, in marginal iodine districts, may have had their iodine balance disturbed from this long unsuspected source.

Other glycosidal substances which cause considerable trouble in the blood-stream are the saponins. They cause haemolysis, or breakdown of the red blood corpuscles, and are found in many common plants such as chickweed and corn cockle. In some quarters it has been suggested that saponin poisoning may cause such conditions as acetonaemia, bloat, etc.

PLANT ALKALOIDS

Alkaloids are complex basic chemical substances, the products of plant metabolism, and their function in living plants is very imperfectly understood. They are produced only by comparatively few of the world's plants, and one plant may produce more than one alkaloid. Hemlock produces five of them.

On the other hand, the same alkaloid may be present in members of widely differing botanical families which bear no relationship to each other. Ephedrine, for instance, is found in both monkshood and yew as well as in the Chinese plant ephedra from which it was originally isolated. Generally, the name of an alkaloid ends in 'ine' and usually bears some relationship to the Latin botanical name of the plant from which it was first obtained. Thus atropine was from *Atropa belladonna*, the deadly nightshade; nicotine from *Nicotiana tabacum*, tobacco; and strychnine from *Strychnos nux-vomica*. Morphine, however, takes its name from Morpheus, the god of sleep, to whom the opium poppy was dedicated in ancient times. Many alkaloids can by synthesized by the chemist, and a large industry has grown up, which prepares them for medicinal and other uses, either from the plants or artificially.

Each alkaloid has its own specific effect on the animal body; many are quite harmless, but others are deadly. Their clinical actions vary considerably among the different animal species to which they may be given. Morphine, for instance, given to man or dog induces sleep, but, given to horse or cat may produce such uncontrollable excitement that the poor creature may damage itself irreparably. Individuals vary more in their susceptibility to the effects of alkaloids than to most other poisons. This may be instanced in the case of nicotine, when the fat cigar inhaled and enjoyed by one may produce much personal discomfort in another. Individuals may develop a tolerance to them after a time, but there is no immunity, and as they are eliminated, the body may develop a craving for more.

No hard and fast rules can be laid down for the treatment of alkaloidal poisoning. In some instances it is necessary to administer another alkaloid which has a directly opposite action, and in others there seems to be no specific or even palliative antidote; the effects must be allowed to subside as the poison is eliminated and the patient treated in accordance with his symptoms.

PHOTO-DYNAMIC SUBSTANCES AND PHOTO-SENSITIZATION

Photo-dynamic substances obtained from plants are mostly coloured, and all of them fluoresce in ultra-violet light. They are capable of passing through the bowel wall into the blood-stream and they exert a sensitizing action on the skin of animals when exposed to strong sunlight. Heavily pigmented skins, and skins covered with pigmented hair, filter out the damaging rays and remain unharmed. In contradistinction to true sunburn, the effective wave-lengths of the light differ, so that sunburn does not affect a creature to which light has passed through ordinary window glass. But to the animal which has become 'photo-sensitized', window glass is no protection. Photo-sensitization is not so commonly seen in the British Isles as in countries where the sunshine is more intense, but there are few markets in this country through which a number of recovered or partially recovered animals do not pass every year on their way to slaughter. As a general rule, evidence of liver dysfunction, and commonly jaundice as the result of it, is seen concurrently with or before the skin injury. The white parts of the skin die and slough off, leaving slow-healing wounds which, even after they are healed, show hairless scars. The udder and teats, and often the muzzle and rims of the eyelids, present particular difficulties in the treatment of animals with no protective pigments in these regions, which even when normal are very sensitive to pain.

There are many fluorescent substances which are normally eaten without causing photo-sensitization because of digestive changes or their inability to pass through the bowel wall, and which, if injected directly into the blood-steam, will almost immediately sensitize the recipient to light; the most notable of them is chlorophyll, the green colouring matter of plants. Under certain circumstances, however, incomplete catabolism of chlorophyll by a dysfunctioning liver may result in the formation of another fluorescent substance; phylloerythrin, which is set free to circulate in the blood-stream. Phylloerythrin thus becomes the substance responsible for photo-sensitization by many of the grasses and fodder plants which under normal conditions are harmless.

Substances which are capable of causing the primary liver damage and dysfunction of the type responsible for the formation of phylloerythrin are varied. A number of them are known while others, without doubt, still await identification. Examples of those which are known include some of the alkaloids present in ergot, certain glycosides and saponins and the toxin of certain strains of a fungus, *Pithomyces chartarum*, a saprophyte which grows upon dead pasture plants. The rye-grass pastures of New Zealand favour its growth and sporulation and its spores, moved as dust from the dead mat at the plant base, settle on the green leaves with which they are eaten by grazing sheep. The toxin set free is responsible for causing the photo-sensitization called 'facial eczema' of sheep in New Zealand where the disease has been a major problem for many years.

Certain drugs can have a similar effect. Of these, the best known is phenothiazine, a medicament which has been used in large quantities for the treatment for worms in mammals and poultry throughout the world. This must be borne in mind when enquiring into cases of photo-sensitization. The author has in his possession photographs of four-day old West African calves suffering from the results of acute photo-sensitization. This could only be ascribed to the dosing of their dams with finely divided phenothiazine within three days prior to parturition. Whether they had become photo-sensitized in utero or had acquired the sensitizing agent via the colostrum after birth is impossible to say.

Of the British plants which are likely to cause photo-sensitization, buckwheat (*Fagopyrum esculcutum*), St. John's wort (*Hypericum perforatum*), and the bog asphodel (*Narthecium ossifragum*) are the best known. There are many others which are suspect, particularly some of the yellow trefoils. The plants which are responsible for 'yellowsis' in Scottish sheep have not yet been identified.

Treatment consists of keeping affected animals indoors in darkened houses, a change of diet, and the administration of medicaments which increase the liver action and bile flow. Aloes and anthracene purgatives should be avoided. Any animal with white skin parts which shows the slightest jaundicing during the hot summer months should be kept in a darkened house until there are signs of recovery.

PHYTO-TOXINS

The phyto-toxins are similar in their effects to bacterial toxins, and if taken in minute doses can produce a true immunity. Serum can be produced to protect against their effect in a manner similar to the preparation of anti-sera for the treatment of such diseases as tetanus and diphtheria. The 'bean' of the castor oil plant (*Ricinus communis*) produces a toxin, ricin, and has caused poisoning of British livestock through its inclusion in imported cattle cakes and meals.

CARCINOGENS

The presence of carcinogens, or factors which are capable of producing cancer, has been demonstrated in such widely differing products of plant origin as tobacco smoke and the fronds of bracken, as well as in aflatoxin (the complex of toxins produced by *Aspergillus flavus*). Considerably more research is required before the actual carcinogenic substances themselves are isolated and identified.

MINERAL POISONS

Mineral poisoning through plants is not so common in Britain as in many other countries. Plants take up minerals from soils in which there is an excess, and in this way poison the animals which feed on them. In some of the southern counties of Britain 'teart pastures' are known, and they induce diarrhoea and wasting through an excess of molybdenum. In America, poisoning with selenium is brought about in the same way, and from many parts of the world come reports of poisoning by the nitrates and nitrites of potassium, taken up in excess by such widely differing plants as oats, beet, turnips and kale.

Poisoning of livestock grazing in the vicinity of industrial areas has occurred through the ingestion of lead and fluorine. These two minerals are deposited from the atmosphere on to the surface of the leaves of grasses and fodder plants. Hay made from them, unless well washed with rain, is as poisonous as the fresh plant. Few plants themselves are able to take up excessive amounts of either lead or fluorine from soils which contain them in large quantities.

DEFICIENCY DISEASES

Illness occurs in animals which have been fed for long periods on grasses or other plants which do not contain sufficient of the substances necessary for health. This may be due to the plants themselves not producing a sufficiency during growth. Under normal conditions of British farming, however, animals are seldom fed for long periods solely upon the products of one species of plant, and such deficiencies, when known, are generally rectified by concurrently feeding oilcake or other supplements.

Mineral deficiency diseases occur when the soils, on which grasses or other fodder plants are grown, do not contain a sufficiency of minerals in a form which the plants can take up, and thus deficiency occurs in both the plants and the animals which feed on them. An example of this type of disease is 'pine' of cattle and sheep caused by cobalt deficiency.

SWEET CLOVER DISEASE

Sweet clover disease, as seen in America, differs from most other forms of plant poisoning. In this instance the non-poisonous substance, coumarin, is broken down into dicoumarol when sweet clover is damaged by the weather and badly harvested. Dicoumarol seriously reduces the clotting powers of the blood, and affected animals may quickly bleed to death from very small wounds.

Dicoumarol is used medicinally for conditions where it is necessary to prevent the formation of blood clots and, because of this action on the blood, similar or related compounds are used as vermin poisons.

About Plant Poisoning

IRRITANT AND SELECTIVE POISONS

The great majority of plant poisons are *irritants;* they cause inflammation of those tissues with which they come in contact. The first parts of the body they affect are the skin and the lining membranes of the mouth, stomach, and bowels. They may be absorbed into the blood-stream from either the undamaged or damaged surface of any or all of these parts.

Poisons which enter the blood-stream circulate throughout the body and thus may affect any part of it. Many of them, particularly the alkaloids, affect specialized body cells to a greater extent than they affect others. Such poisons are said to be *selective* in their action.

Selective poisons which affect the brain and spinal cord – the centres controlling all body functions and movements – may, by injuring these parts, cause paralysis or impaired or excessive function of any organ or limb, according to which part of the brain or spinal cord is affected. Poisons which cause their effects in this way are said to have a *central* or *central nervous* action. Those which circulate and cause damage to the blood vessels, the heart, or other organs as they pass through them, are said to have a *direct* action on the parts they affect.

ELIMINATION OF POISONS FROM THE BODY

Poisons which are absorbed into the blood-stream are eliminated from the body by the kidneys, and sometimes in smaller amounts in the saliva, the breath, the sweat, and the milk. Those which cannot pass unchanged through the kidneys are, in most instances, either neutralized by combining with some part of the blood to form a compound which the kidneys can remove or, alternatively, they may be detoxicated and broken down by the liver into substances which can be excreted. During the process of detoxication the liver may suffer severe damage and the breakdown products may seriously injure the kidneys and urinary tract as they pass through, during excretion. Liver damage may be manifested when symptoms of jaundice appear, the mucous membranes of the mouth and eyes become yellow and the urine dark coloured, while the colour of the faeces becomes paler. Injury to the kidneys is indicated by tenderness over the loins, diuresis, blood-stained urine, and sometimes by the total suppression of urine.

Blood-sugar or glucose is necessary to aid the liver in the process of detoxication and to prevent damage to its tissues. For this reason glucose solutions are often injected directly into the blood-stream of patients by doctors and veterinary surgeons. Household sugar, molasses and starch all have a similar effect, but their action is much slower, because they must be given by the mouth and converted by digestion into simple sugars before they can be absorbed into the blood. They are all extremely valuable in the treatment of poisoned patients, and are given to maintain a steady supply of blood-sugar to the liver. Which particular one of them is used, depends upon the state of the patient's bowels at the time; starch or wheat-flour gruels are desirable in cases of diarrhoea; molasses and golden syrup, being slightly laxative, are better used when there is constipation; and household sugar, having little effect one way or the other, may be given at any time.

CUMULATIVE POISONS

A readily absorbed poison which cannot be detoxicated by the liver and which can only be excreted very slowly by the kidneys is, without doubt, the most damaging of all. The ingestion of an excessive quantity of such a poison invariably leads to acute symptoms and death but, in many instances, one very small dose may produce no visible effect. Should successive small doses be taken continuously over a period, however, and the rate of intake be even only slightly in excess of that of excretion, there occurs a gradual build-up of poison in the body until sufficient has accumulated to manifest symptoms. Any poison which behaves in this way is said to have a *cumulative* effect.

Recovery and convalescence are always slow in patients affected by one of the cumulative poisons. Care to prevent more of the poisonous substance being taken is essential, because only a very small amount may be needed to cause a recurrence of serious trouble. Convalescent animals should be encouraged to drink as much water or other liquids as possible, in order to assist excretion of the poison through the urine.

About Poisoned Animals

SUDDEN DEATH

The main causes of the sudden death of apparently healthy animals are hypo-magnesaemia, accident, lightning stroke, poisoning and anthrax. In all cases of sudden death it is the statutory duty of the owner to ascertain that the animal did not die from a scheduled contagious disease. Unless he has direct evidence to the countrary, he should suspect that cattle, sheep, and goats died from anthrax and poultry from fowl pest. The carcass must not be disposed of until after it has been examined by a veterinary surgeon, nor should any persons or animals be allowed access to it.

The diagnosis of scheduled contagious disease has been a free service by the State for over a century, and the machinery for the examination of carcasses is immediately set in motion by reporting the death to the nearest police constable. Anthrax diagnosis takes priority over most other diseases, and no avoidable delay is ever allowed in making the examination. There can be no excuse for failure to carry out this obligation, and the animal owner who fails to do so and allows an anthrax-infected carcass to go to a knackery is a public menace. No casual or external examination of a whole carcass can completely indicate the cause of death; post-mortem changes and decomposition mask it still further. Only after anthrax has been negatived microscopically is it permissible, or safe, for post-mortem examinations to be made of cattle, sheep or goats, which have been found dead, and this is particularly so if there is blood from the nose or anus.

The poisonous plants which are most likely to cause sudden death in animals are the yew tree and those plants which contain cyanogenetic glycosides.

SALIVATION

Salivation, slavering, or slobbering, may be seen early in cases of poisoning. In the majority of instances it is due to the irritant action of the poison on the lining of the mouth. In a few cases it may be due to the central action of the poison, but with most British plants this is rare. Salivation may be due to other causes, such as wounds, foreign bodies and, in cattle, actinomycosis or 'wooden tongue'. Foot-and-mouth disease must also be considered, but with this disease there is usually lameness as well.

VOMITING

Vomiting is chiefly due to irritation of the lining of the stomach. In man, the dog, and the pig, vomiting is comparatively easy, and in suspected cases of poisoning, if they have not vomited already, an *emetic* should be given to induce them to do so. The simplest and most easily procured emetic for children consists of one or two teaspoonfuls of common salt in a glass of water; for dogs, a large crystal of washing soda, introduced down the throat in the same way as a pill, is the most satisfactory emetic. Neither salt nor soda should be given to a pig; apomorphine is probably the best for this animal, but the drug should be administered only as a hypodermic injection by a veterinary surgeon.

Persistent vomiting in children, dogs and pigs may be due to the central action of the poison, but it is more commonly due to irritation. Attempts may be made to allay this condition by giving, as a demulcent, albumen water with glucose or sugar. This is made by adding the white of one egg and a dessertspoonful of sugar or glucose to half a pint of cold water; a pinch of salt makes the mixture more palatable. A little should be given at a time, and if it is thrown back again it may bring some of the poisonous substances with it. It should be repeated five minutes after each bout of retching finishes, and should be continued in this way until it is retained for half an hour. Thereafter, hourly doses are usually sufficient to prevent the return of distressing symptoms.

Horses cannot vomit without injury to the entrance of the stomach, and if this happens it usually results in death. Owing to the long soft palate of the horse, anything which is regurgitated must come through the nose. Those who have once heard the piteous scream of a poisoned horse in its futile attempts to vomit can never forget it.

Cattle, sheep and goats seldom vomit. When they do, it is usually done with great force; and cattle vomit with less distress than goats. Sheep are usually very distressed and may almost scream in their attempts. Few plants cause vomiting or retching in horses and ruminants; the one most likely to do so is rhododendron.

ABDOMINAL PAIN OR COLIC

Colic, as a symptom of poisoning, is not unusual in animals, and by observation of their behaviour it is often possible to get some indication of the part of the alimentary tract in which the pain is most severe.

Pain in the stomach and small intestines of the horse or the pig is indicated by great uneasiness. They lie for a short while and then attempt to sit up on their haunches, in the same position as a sitting dog. Ruminants with pain in their complicated stomachs either stand or lie in the normal position and grunt as they breathe out. Any hyper-acute inflammation of the fourth stomach (abomasum or rennet stomach) of ruminants may be accompanied by convulsions or fits, which may be followed by cerebral haemorrhage and death. The haemorrhage is most commonly found at post-mortem examination in the region of the circulus arteriosus or Circle of Willis.

When the pain is in the large intestine, all animals are much alike in the symptoms they show. They attempt to lie in unnatural positions, groan, roll on their backs, and kick at their bellies.

Sweating usually accompanies colicky pains in the horse and sometimes in the pig, but noticeable sweating on the bodies of ruminants or dogs is almost unknown.

Abdominal pain is seldom due to the central action of poisons; it is most commonly the result of direct irritation of the nerve endings of the alimentary system. To remedy it, the irritating substance must be removed, either by causing it to pass along the alimentary tract and out with the faeces, or, from the stomach, by washing out or by operation. In the case of a few poisons, a specific substance is known which will neutralize them, but this is far from common. Demulcents or substances which have a soothing action on the inflamed walls of the alimentary tract are of great value in easing pain.

EMPTYING THE STOMACH OF POISONS

The stomach pump is commonly used to empty and wash out the stomachs of poisoned human beings and dogs; after this has been done it is usual to leave in some inert substance which adsorbs, or attracts to its surface, any remaining poisonous substances. The adsorbents most often used are animal charcoal (bone black) and kaolin (fuller's earth). Adsorbents are of great value in the treatment of pigs and dogs after they have vomited and also in the treatment of horses; they are of little use, however, in the treatment of the ruminants at any time. Kaolin or animal charcoal may be given with liquid paraffin, or suspended in milk or thin gruel. The use of the stomach pump for washing out the stomach of pigs is also anatomically possible, but, in actual practice, it can seldom be done without the prior administration of deep narcosis or a general anaesthetic.

The stomachs of horses and ruminants are never completely empty during life. Should they be emptied, and the contents not be immediately replaced by something else, the animals collapse and die in a very short time. Attempts are sometimes made to wash out the stomach of the horse, although it is seldom practicable. Should it be done, however, the contents may be replaced with fine bran suspended in thin oatmeal gruel and milk, to which eggs, sugar, and charcoal or kaolin may be added.

Stomach-pumping is of little or no use in removing the rumen contents of cattle, sheep, or goats. In these animals the operation of rumenotomy (opening the rumen via the left flank) presents the only practicable solution to the problem, if the number of affected animals is not too great.

When rumenotomy is to be performed for the removal of poisonous plants, all the rumen contents must be removed and replaced with fresh foodstuffs, and the owner is well advised to have ready hay chaff, mixed with bran and crushed oats, scalded with boiling water and kept at about body temperature until the operator calls for it. Three large stable-bucketfuls of this mixture are not too much for a medium-sized cow, and the operator will advise if he requires eggs, milk, sugar, or yeast, to be mixed with it, but these need not be added until the last moment.

IRRITANT POISONS: TREATMENT WITH DEMULCENTS

Demulcents are agents which soothe and relieve irritation of such mucous surfaces as the lining membranes of the mouth, stomach, and bowels. In all cases of irritant poisoning, demulcents should be given at the earliest possible moment. In the first instance, a mixture of eggs, sugar and milk is best. Others, like linseed tea and gruels of oatmeal, flour and starch, may be given later.

The proteins of egg and raw milk are often coagulated or curdled by the more irritant poisons, and when this happens they bind up some of the poisonous substances and render them less harmful. This action is very valuable, even though at times it may have only a temporary effect. They also help to protect and to promote the healing of raw and ulcerating surfaces.

Glucose and sugar assist the liver in detoxicating the poison and so help to prevent liver damage. They prevent the exhaustion of the patient by acting as sources of quickly available energy and, being slightly antiseptic, help to prevent the invasion of raw surfaces by bacteria.

The quantity of egg, sugar, and milk mixture to be given to an animal depends upon its size.

Cows require a dozen eggs, one pound of sugar and half a gallon of skimmed or whole milk; yearlings need about half of this, and sheep and goats about a quarter.

Horses and medium-sized pigs, having smaller stomachs and being more awkward to dose, require three eggs and two ounces of sugar made up with milk to half a pint. This is sufficient at one time for these two animals, but the dose may be repeated after half an hour. If a larger dose is needed for a horse, the veterinary surgeon will probably administer it by stomach tube.

The administration of medicines to sick pigs may present a problem to those unused to handling these animals. The method which occasions least distress is to approach the animal quietly while it is lying down, and with a tablespoon pour a little into the side of the mouth, repeating the process after each swallow. In this way excitement and exhaustion are avoided, as well as suffocation, which often occurs when pigs are forcibly drenched.

DIARRHOEA

Diarrhoea is occasionally the result of poisoning by substances which act on the nervous system, but more often it is due to direct irritation of the bowel wall. The inflamed bowel is unable to absorb the liquids contained in it and they pass directly out. In severe cases of enteritis or inflammation of the bowels, liquids may be withdrawn from the blood, and if the inflammatory process goes deeper still, blood itself may be exuded.

Diarrhoea is nature's way of speedily removing irritating substances from the bowels, and in the early stages of poisoning no attempt should be made to check it.

Should it be persistent and the animal become exhausted from dehydration or loss of body fluids, every attempt must be made to increase the patient's resistance by giving astringents. Milk which has been boiled and allowed to cool, cold gruel of flour and starch, eggs, and occasionally alcoholic liquors like brandy and whisky, are all helpful.

CONSTIPATION

Stasis, or lack of muscular movement of the bowels, may occur when poisons which act on the nervous system paralyse the nerves which supply the bowel walls. When stasis occurs it is usual to give alkaloids or substances which have a specific action on the affected nerves or nerve centres.

Constipation occurs when the bowel wall absorbs too much of the liquid content or when the fluid intake is too low. In these conditions laxatives are usually given, and the use of liquid paraffin (medicinal paraffin, *not lamp oil*) cannot be too strongly recommended for poisoned animals. It is an excellent lubricant and is not absorbed from the bowel; it protects the bowel wall from further irritation and, in many forms of poisoning, prevents further absorption of the poison into the blood-stream. It does not cause the nausea which is so often seen after dosing with linseed oil, nor the constipation which follows the action of castor oil. Liquid paraffin has its faults, however; being almost tasteless, animals do not swallow it readily, especially if warmed and it should therefore be given as *cold* as possible and with a few drops of turpentine or ether added to give it a taste.

Drastic purgation is definitely contra-indicated in all forms of plant poisoning, and such medicaments as Epsom salts, aloes, physic balls, or proprietary purgatives should never be given to any poisoned animal, unless prescribed by the veterinary surgeon in attendance.

Laxative diets for poisoned animals may include molasses or golden syrup, yeast, warm linseed tea, hay tea, calf-rearing gruel, oatmeal gruel, and warm fresh milk.

CONVULSIONS OR FITS

These are usually seen only in the late stages of poisoning and are the result of serious affection of the central nervous system by the poison. Death may occur during a convulsion or a period of coma, or deep unconsciousness may intervene.

CESSATION OF RUMINATION OR 'LOSS OF THE CUD'

The commonest sequel to poisoning of cattle, sheep and goats, is cessation or suspension of rumination or cud-chewing. The peculiar arrangement of the digestive tract of these ruminants, which have no digestive juices in the first three compartments of their complicated stomach, makes it necessary to remind readers that any digestion or breakdown of foodstuffs in these organs is the result of action by the bacteria, yeasts, and animalcules which normally live there in a delicately balanced community. After an animal has suffered from poisoning, many of the least resistant of these microscopic creatures will have died out, and rumination or cud-chewing is suspended until fermentation and the balance between them are restored.

In cases where acids have been used to counteract the poisons, or where the plants themselves have contained an excess of acid, it is essential to give something which will set up fermentation in an acid medium, and for this purpose bakers' yeast is outstanding in its effects; cattle require about one pound, broken down in lukewarm water.

Should the medication have been alkaline in reaction, the alkalinity of the stomach contents must be neutralized before fermentation can begin. To achieve this, one pound of sugar dissolved in one pint of vinegar may be given to a cow.

Sheep and goats take doses proportionate to their size of these harmless, but very efficient, remedies.

One dose is usually sufficient to restore rumination, but if necessary it may be repeated on several successive days.

Should it become necessary to reinoculate the rumen contents with normal organisms, it may be done very simply by taking a cud from the mouth of a healthy animal and introducing it down the throat of the sick one.

ANAEMIA AND DEBILITY

Anaemia and debility are common sequels to those types of poisoning in which there has been loss of blood or destruction of the red blood corpuscles. In most cases where this has occurred the body reserves of the amino-acids, proteins and minerals essential for health have been depleted, and they must be replaced by feeding with a generous high-protein diet to which minerals have been added. For this purpose most of the reputable brands of commercial mineral mixture are quite satisfactory. Common salt is necessary to restore the balance of the body fluids, and iron is needed to rebuild the haemoglobin of the red blood corpuscles.

When giving iron salts in tonics, it is best to make certain that the catalysts, copper and cobalt, are present, by adding traces of them to the mixture. If they are deficient the body is unable to make use of the iron and it is wasted.

Fungi

MOULDS AND ERGOT

ALTHOUGH for many years the study of mycosis, or disease caused by the actual invasion of body tissues by pathogenic fungi, has received considerable attention from research workers and clinicians, the study of mycotoxicosis, or disease caused by mycotoxins or products elaborated by fungal growth outside the body, has, until comparatively recent times, been almost neglected. The effects of some of these substances, such as ergot alkaloids, have been known and used in medicine for many centuries and, today, there can be few households in which one or more of its members or their animals have not, at some time, been dosed with penicillin or some similar product of fungal growth or its synthetic equivalent. From the search for new antibiotics for the cure of disease, there must be a great wealth of accumulated knowledge hidden away in the archives and laboratories of the larger chemical manufacturers of the effects upon laboratory animals of the products of many species of fungi and, from this, there may well be, some day, a breakthrough on the causation of well recognized syndromes of presently unknown etiology. For instance, that bugbear of New Zealand flockmasters known as 'facial eczema' of sheep, a form of photo-sensitization which for long defied all attempts to find a cause, is now known to be the result of the ingestion of a fungus, *Pithomyces chartarum* (Berk. & Curt.) M. B. Ellis, which is saprophytic upon dead rye-grass and other species of pasture plants. The conditions which prevail over a short period of the year are highly favourable for its growth and sporulation, and the spores, formed on the dead leaves at the base of the plant after it has died down for the winter, rise as a dust and contaminate the new green leaves of the next year's growth and are eaten by the grazing sheep. The toxin they contain not only causes severe damage to the liver of the sheep but may also affect kidneys and adrenal glands in addition. An affected liver becomes incapable of performing the complete catabolism of chlorophyll and this results in the formation of a fluorescent photo-sensitizing substance, phyllo-erythrin, which is set free to circulate in the blood-stream.

The sparsely covered and more exposed parts of the face and ears thus become sensitive to light and damage to the skin of these parts gives the disease its not particularly apt name of 'facial eczema' which, in reality, is but a secondary manifestation of a diseased liver. *P. chartarum*, in common with almost every other vegetable producer of toxin, varies considerably from strain to strain in the quantity of toxin it elaborates and this, in large measure, accounts for the wide variation in the degree of its effects.

From almost every country clinical reports of acute and chronic illness, which has resulted from feeding mouldy fodder or grain to farm animals, have become almost commonplace but, unfortunately, except for saying that the food was mouldy and describing the symptoms, few of them have gone very far into the taxonomy of the organism concerned nor has there been much research into its toxicity. Those most commonly implicated belong to the genera *Aspergillus*, *Fusarium*, *Mucor*, *Penicillium*, *Pithomyces*, *Thermopolyspora* *Micromonospora* and *Diplodia*. There are few signs or symptoms that an animal can exhibit which have not been described as due to mycotoxicosis. They have varied from mild indigestion to acute colic and diarrhoea, nervous twitching to convulsions, incoordination to complete paralysis, blindness, coma, sudden death, haemoglobinuria, haemoglobinaemia, diuresis, constipation, pulmonary oedema, pulmonary emphysema and abortion.

ASPERGILLUS SPP.

In Italy, as long ago as the beginning of the present century, toxic substances were extracted from *Aspergillus fumigatus* Fres. This species is not only capable of producing mycotoxicosis but is commonly the cause of the mycosis called Aspergillosis as well. Aspergillosis is chiefly a lung condition affecting both birds and mammals, including man. The acute disease is characterized by pneumonia but in its more chronic form the patient coughs and becomes emaciated. The disease runs a course very similar to pulmonary tuberculosis for which it might be mistaken clinically and at post-mortem examination. When viewed by the naked eye, the nodules in the lungs are almost impossible to differentiate from those of tuberculosis but there are many differences when smears are viewed under the microscope and the hyphae of the mould show in profusion throughout the slide. Mouldy corn and fodder are the main sources of this infection and the spores are carried into the lungs by inhalation. The infection is more likely to occur when mouldy foods are given indoors in damp ill-ventilated buildings where winds and draughts do not disperse the spores.

Another species, *Aspergillus flavus* Link ex Fr., has long been blamed in America for causing a form of meningo-encephalitis or 'blind-staggers' in horses. Latterly, it has returned to prominence once more as the cause of a mycotoxic disease of turkey poults which affected birds on a number of farms and produced an estimated death-roll of at least one hundred thousand of them. A further outbreak of a similar disease of ducklings and young pheasants, in which about ten thousand ducklings were lost on one farm alone, led to the discovery that groundnuts, infected with *A. flavus*, were the cause of the condition. At first it was thought that the toxicity was confined to groundnuts from Brazil but it was soon evident that infected nuts were to be found in most African countries too. Hyphae of the mould are found in the substance of the kernel of infected nuts; these may be picked out by the naked eye from non-infected, by the discolouration of the flesh which, instead of being its normal white, has become yellow or brownish.

The toxic principles of *A. flavus*, like those of most other poisonous organisms, are not one simple substance but a complex of at least six separate entities which have been grouped together under the name of 'aflatoxin'. Here again, the strain of the mould is at least as important as its species, from the point of view of toxin production. Some strains are able to produce large quantities of aflatoxin while others appear to be relatively harmless, although both are of the same species and are grown in the same environment.

Susceptibility to aflatoxin varies considerably with the species of animal. In calves the clinical symptoms and post mortem lesions in the liver are typically those of ragwort poisoning, although K. R. Hill was able to differentiate cellular variations microscopically.

In pigs the main features of the disease are jaundice, enlargement of the liver and subcutaneous haemorrhages, while sheep appear to be far more resistant to its effects than most other animals. Chickens, too, appear to be more resistant than turkey poults and ducklings, in which the disease is characterized by depression, staggering gait and often sudden death. At post-mortem examination, the carcass is usually found to be congested and oedematous and the liver enlarged, firm and pale. Many affected ducklings also have extensive subcutaneous haemorrhages along the back, legs and feet. Microscopically, the liver lesions indicate toxic damage; there is degeneration of the parenchyma and rapid proliferation of bile ductule epithelium. It has also been said that aflatoxin may have carcinogenic properties.

The author is not aware of any recorded instance of human poisoning by aflatoxin.

Thermophilic moulds, or those which develop at high temperatures, are to be found in hay which has 'heated' in the rick or bale. They may also be found in unsealed tower silos which are used for moist-storage of unripened barley. Of these moulds, *Thermopolyspora polyspora* Henssen and *Thermoactinomyces vulgaris* Tsilinksy are responsible for causing 'farmers' lung', an allergic condition which may be set off by inhaling spores in dust from mouldy hay. Attacks usually develop five or six hours after exposure to the dust or they may appear without any known history of exposure. Sudden asthmatic types of attack are not a feature of the disease. Pepys and Jenkins (1966) describe both systemic and pulmonary reactions. In the former, fever, shivering attacks, malaise and loss of weight are experienced; in the latter, coughing, dyspnoea, crepitant rales and defective gas exchange are found.

Precipitins in the serum of those affected may be demonstrated against antigens prepared from mouldy hay and the same authors (1965) found similar reactions to the same antigens in the sera of cattle affected with indoor fog fever, an acute respiratory disease which is characterized by pulmonary oedema and emphysema.

Traditionally, many generations of horsemen have blamed dust from mouldy hay for causing 'broken wind' or pulmonary emphysema in horses.

As a preventative measure, in the larger industrial studs where there was adequate machinery for the preparation of horse food in bulk, all unmilled grain and newly cut hay or straw chaff was passed through a dust extractor before being conveyed to mill or mixer. Even so, he was considered to be a poor stableman who, at the first sound of a sneeze in the stable, omitted to dampen the mixed corn sufficiently to prevent dust from rising and being inhaled while the horse was feeding.

ERGOT (*Claviceps* spp.)

Ergot is a fungus which is parasitic, chiefly upon members of the grass family. In Britian, *Claviceps purpurea* (Fr.) Tul., which may affect rye, barley and other cereal crops, is the species usually held responsible for most cases of ergotism or ergot poisoning but other species, in other countries, are also known to produce similar effects. In New Zealand, *C. paspali* Stev. & Hall, parasitic upon paspalum grass and, in America, several other species of ergot which affect pasture grasses, cause between them considerable annual loss in animal production. The ergots are the sclerotia or fruiting bodies of the fungus. They are about $\frac{1}{3}$–1$\frac{1}{2}$ inches long, slender, curved and tapering at both ends. They are dark violet to black in colour on the outside but whitish or pinkish-white on the inside. They have a characteristic disagreeable fishy taste and odour.

Ergot contains a large series of alkaloids, some of which are toxic and others which are pharmacologically inert. Extracts of ergot and preparations of the alkaloids are used very considerably in medicine, chiefly for their action on the muscles of the womb and in the treatment of migraine.

Human poisoning by ergot may be the result of overdosing with medicinal preparations or by eating it in bread made from ergotized grain. In the latter instance the condition is acute, and whole families, even whole villages of people, may become affected. In olden times, ergotism or ergot poisoning was thought to be a visitation of God and was known as St. Anthony's Fire, because the saint was reputed to have suffered in this way.

The acute form is characterized by a burning sensation in the mouth, stomach, and extremeties, with abdominal pains and vomiting. Impaired vision and hallucinations are accompanied by spasmodic contractions of the limbs, and in the last stages these are followed by convulsions.

In the chronic form, which occurs when smaller amounts are eaten over a longer period, there are acute pains in the extremities followed by dry gangrene, due to the contraction of the smaller blood vessels and diminished blood supply to the parts. The limb is almost intolerably painful, but the actual sloughing parts are anaesthetized.

Although the ergot alkaloids have a direct action on the muscular walls of the womb after the commencement of labour, their reputation as abortifacients is totally unwarranted and undeserved, for their action on the pregnant but quiescent womb is, for all practical purposes, non-existent. Abortion among farm animals suffering from ergotism is a rarity and, if it occurs at all, is more than likely to be due to some other factor. In an outbreak seen by the author, pregnant dairy cows and a sow, all of which had been fed on ergotized barley meal, carried their young to term, although they had lost part of their tails and ears, as well as having large gangrenous wounds in their heels.

Ergotism in the domesticated animals occurs in the chronic form of the disease more commonly than in the acute form: the reason being that one type of grain seldom forms the major part of the diet of animals, as does bread in the case of many human beings.

Symptoms in animals may be lameness and dry gangrene of the end of the tail, tips of the ears and sometimes the lips and tip of the tongue. The most common site of gangrene in the limbs of cows seen by the author was in the heels, and several cows and the sow mentioned above, lost their supernumerary digits.

Poultry are quickly affected by ergotism and suffer from gangrene of the comb and wattles and often of the tongue. As the case goes on, they may lose one or several of their toes.

O'Neil and Rae (1965) state that chickens cannot tolerate more than 0·3 per cent of ergot in their ration. Hens tolerated from 0·2 per cent to 0·4 per cent but higher levels affected egg production and the maintenance of body weight. Contrary to chicks, mortality was not observed with hens when fed diets containing as much as 9·0 per cent ergot.

First-aid treatment of chronic cases in animals consists of changing the diet immediately. Little else can be done, except to take care that the gangrenous parts do not become septic from outside infection. This is not always an easy matter in the hind legs and tails of cattle and pigs.

For further reading

MYCOTOXICOSIS—GENERAL

M. CRAWFORD, 1962, *Vet. Bul.* **32.** 415–20.

AFLATOXIN

In cotton-seed cake

R. M. LOOSMORE, R. ALLCROFT, E. A. TUTTON and R. B. A. CARNAGHAN, 1964, *Vet Rec* **76.** 64–5.

Cattle

R. ALLCROFT and G. LEWIS (Addendum by K. R. HILL) 1963, *Vet. Rec.* **75.** 487–94.

Toxicity

P. K. C. Austwick and G. AYERST, 1963, *Chem. and Ind.* Jan. 55–61.

Chemistry

K. SARGEANT, R. B. A. CARNAGHAN, R. ALLCROFT, 1963, *Chem. and Ind.* Jan. 53–5.

Metabolism in sheep

R. ALLCROFT, H. ROGERS, G. LEWIS, J. NABNEY and P. E. BEST, 1966, *Nature, Lond.* **209.** 154–5.

Action on liver

K. R. REES, 1966, *Proc. Roy. Soc. Med.* **59.** 755–7.

THERMOPHILIC MOULDS

Farmer's lung

J. PEPYS and P. A. JENKINS, 1966. *Proc. Roy. Soc. Med.* **59.** 1007.

In fog fever

A. MACKENZIE *ibid.* 1008–12.

P. A. JENKINS and J. PEPYS, 1965, *Vet. Rec.* **77.** 464–6.

ERGOT

Cattle

F. J. MADDEN, 1941, *Yearb. Insp. Stk. N.S.W.*, 35.

Agric. Gaz. N.S.W., 1942. **53.** 384.

Sheep

J. J. CUNNINGHAM, J. B. SWAN and C. S. M. HOPKIRK, 1944, *N.Z. J. Sci. Tech., Sect. A.* **26.** 121–36.

Meat and milk
I. J. Cunningham, J. B. Swan and C. S. M. Hopkirk, 1944, *N.Z. J. Sci. Tech., Sect. A.* **26.** 121–4.
Alkaloids
C. H. Hassall, 1944, *N.Z. J. Sci. Tech., Sect. B.* **25.** 169–74.
Pigs and experimental animals
A. W. Nordskog and R. T. Clark, 1945. *Amer. J. vet. Res.* **6.** 107–16.
Toxic effects
I. Rosenfeld and O. A. Beath, 1950, *J. Amer. vet. med. Ass.* **116.** 308–11.
J. B. O'Neil and W. J. Rae, 1965, *Poultry Sci.* **44.** 1404.

THE LARGER FUNGI

The Larger Fungi, more commonly known as 'mushrooms' and 'toadstools', are not eaten in Britain to the extent that they are eaten in Europe, and consequently, human poisoning by them is of much rarer occurrence. Few Britons eat any fungus other than the Field Mushroom *Agaricus campestris* L. ex Fr. and its cultivated varieties.

There are only a few poisonous British species, and of these, several are extremely dangerous.

Many of the 'safe' species may cause acute indigestion or illness if they are not gathered in good condition or are improperly prepared. Susceptible individuals and those who eat excessive quantities may suffer considerably after eating them.

There is no rough and ready method of assessing the poisonous qualities of fungi; the most poisonous of them peel as easily as the safest, and do not blacken a silver spoon. To rely on such methods is extremely foolhardy, to say the least. Before eating any strange food, it is wise to learn something of its character and appearance, and fungi are no exception to this rule.

Poisoning of the domesticated animals by the larger fungi is rare, and there are only a few recorded instances of which the author is aware.

DEATH CAP (*Amanita phalloides* (Vaill. ex Fr.) Secr.)

Death Cap is the most poisonous of all the fungi and is responsible for over ninety per cent of human deaths from fungus poisoning.

It is about the same size as the field mushroom and is found in woods and adjoining grassland during late summer and autumn. The cap is white to yellow-olive in colour and the gills are white or creamy, never pink or brown as in the Field Mushroom. The most characteristic feature is the volva, a small cup-like socket within which the bottom of the stem rests. It may be necessary to dig up the whole fungus in order to see this.

The poison of the Death Cap is said to be a substance, phalloedin, which has a toxic action on the liver and kidneys causing necrosis and fatty degeneration. In experimental cases in animals, there is a marked decrease in both the sugar and chloride content of the blood.

Poisoning by Death Cap is characterized by a delay of six to fifteen hours between the ingestion of the fungus and the onset of symptoms.

The symptoms of poisoning are acute abdominal pain, diarrhoea, and vomiting with blood in the vomit. These occur in intermittent bouts and cause much distress. They are followed by great prostration. The drawn facial expression of the patient, together with cramp in the calves of the legs, and the abdominal symptoms, are said, in France, to be diagnostic. Cessation of urination, coldness of the skin, jaundice, cyanosis, and coma are followed by death.

Post-mortem examination of human cases reveals ulceration and inflammation of the stomach and bowels, fatty degeneration of the liver, kidneys, and heart, with congestion and haemorrhages in most of the viscera.

Treatment. First-aid treatment is of little avail after the commencement of symptoms. Medical attention is required as early as possible to wash out the stomach and administer other treatment.

In France, because of the immunity of rabbits to this poison, a mixture of five rabbits' stomachs and five rabbits' brains minced together and given to the patient, has achieved some success in the treatment of this deadly condition. In Germany, intravenous injections of large quantities of glucose-saline are said to be of great value.

DESTROYING ANGEL (*Amanita verna* (Bull. ex Fr.) Vitt.)

Destroying Angel is a species closely allied to Death Cap and is poisonous to human beings. Piercy, Hargis, and Brown (1944), have described the poisoning of cattle by *A. verna* in America; they ate the fungus which grew profusely when grass and all other foods were scarce.

With the onset of symptoms, the animals did not lift their tails for defaecation, and as a consequence the buttocks and area surrounding the tail were plastered with a mass of dung of normal consistency. The mucous lining of the rectum was inflamed and had vesicles, papules, and ulcers on its surface, and these sometimes extended to the perineum and vulva. Occasionally the rectum prolapsed. Although there was loss of weight, appetite and rumination were normal until late in the case, when a convulsion preceded death.

Post-mortem examination revealed inflammation throughout the alimentary tract and the mucous membranes were easily rubbed off. There were haemorrhages in the heart and in the liver which was enlarged, the kidneys were pale and the bladder distended with urine.

FLY AGARIC (*Amanita muscaria* (L. ex Fr.) Hook.)

Fly Agaric is the fungus often depicted in fairy-story books because of the beauty of its brilliant scarlet or orange-red cap with white or yellowish-white patches, which are fragments of the volva. It is 8 or 9 inches high and 6–8 inches across. The stem is narrower at the top than at the base, where it forms a bulbous swelling, surrounded by a series of horizontal ridges. The gills, stem, and flesh are white, except immediately under the skin of the cap, where it is slightly yellow.

Fly Agaric is not likely to be eaten in Britain because it 'looks poisonous' and has a bitter taste, but decoctions of the fungus have been used as a fly poison for many generations. Lapps and inhabitants of Northern Siberia prepare a liquor from it which they drink to produce intoxication.

Muscarine stimulates the parasympathetic nerves and is rapidly excreted by the kidneys; it is antagonized by atropine. In large amounts it may cause death, but with smaller amounts intoxication, sweating, salivation, lachrymation, vomiting and diarrhoea occur, the pulse is irregular and is often slowed, the pupils are contracted, and double vision and hallucinations are common. In more acute cases, delirium and convulsions occur. Symptoms appear very rapidly after eating the fungus or drinking the liquor, there is no long delay as with poisoning by Death Cap. In cases which recover, the symptoms pass off again with similar rapidity in a few hours. Greatorex

(1966), describes *A. muscaria* poisoning of a mongrel terrier which first lost its inhibitory control and became vicious when disturbed, and later, within eighteen hours, developed posterior paralysis. After treatment with atropine, the dog had recovered within 60 hours of ingesting the fungus.

PANTHER CAP or False Blusher (*Amanita pantherina* (DC. ex Fr.) Secr.)

The Panther Cap may be eaten in mistake for the true Blusher (*Amanita rubescens* (Pers. ex Fr.) Quél.), an edible species which it somewhat resembles.

It has a dull brown or brown-grey cap with small white patches, and fine grooves around the edge. The gills are white and crowded, and they may touch the stem, when young. The stem is white and swollen at its base, with two or three ridges at the top of the swelling.

The flesh of the Panther Cap is white and does not change colour when cut or broken; this distinguishes it from the Blusher which becomes suffused with a pink or reddish colour in parts where it has been cut or injured.

The Panther Cap contains the alkaloid, muscarine; it is not so poisonous as the Fly Agaric, but if eaten the effects are similar.

MOREL (*Morchella esculenta* Pers. ex St. Amans)

Common morel is an edible fungus which may sometimes be found in woodland clearings during spring. It differs from most of the larger fungi already mentioned both in structure and by bearing its spores in little sacs.

Herms (1950) describes two cases of poisoning of dachshunds by morel although their owners who partook of the same food were unharmed. In the first instance the dog was given broth in which morel had been cooked and, in the second, a piece of the cooked fungus had been given. The symptoms which followed included emesis, slight jaundice, haemoglobinuria and blood-stained diarrhoea. Vomition was controlled by treatment with glucose intravenously and bismuth subnitrate with belladonna orally. The haemoglobinuria subsided in about four days.

OTHER POISONOUS FUNGI

Among other species which are known to be poisonous are Crested Lepiota (*Lepiota cristata* (Fr.) Kummer), Livid Entoloma (*Entoloma sinuatum* (Bull. ex Fr.) Kummer), Red-staining Inocybe (*Inocybe patouillardii* Bres.), Yellow-staining Mushroom (*Agaricus xanthodermus* Genev.) and Verdigris Agaric (*Stropharia aeruginosa* (Curt. ex Fr.) Quél.). None of them is as poisonous as species in the genus *Amanita*.

For further reading

AMANITA PHALLOIDES

C. A. Birch, 1946, *Practitioner*, **157.** 135–40.
J. Dubash and D. Teare, 1946, *Brit. med. J.* Jan. 12th, 45–7.
D. Lewes, 1948, *Brit. med. J.* Aug. 21st, 383.

AMANITA VERNA

P. L. Piercy, G. Hargis and C. A. Brown, 1944, *J. Amer. vet. med. Ass.* **105.** 206–8.

AMANITA MUSCARIA

J. C. Greatorex, 1966, *Vet. Rec.* **78.** 725–6.

MOREL

H. Herms, 1950, *Berl. Münch. tierärtzl. Woch.* (8). 161..

Pteridophyta

EQUISETACEAE

HORSETAILS (*Equisetum* spp.)

Horsetails are widely distributed throughout Britian and are a troublesome weed of damp land, both grazing and arable. There are some ten species of them to be found in this country, and of these the Common Horsetail (*Equisetum arvense* L.) and the Marsh Horsetail (*E. palustre* L.) enjoy almost ubiquitous distribution. The others are more local.

The horsetails are perennials with a creeping rootstock and erect, hollow, jointed stems; there are no leaves and no real flowers. The fruiting of these plants is effected by tiny granules called spores, which are formed on the tops of fruiting stems in a terminal cone, which consists of several whorls of shield-shaped, short-stalked, dark-coloured scales, under each of which lie six or seven spore cases, each packed with minute spores.

The poisonous principle of horsetail withstands the temperatures reached during the making and storage of hay and it is from feeding upon hay containing large quantities of horsetail during autumn and winter that the majority of cases of poisoning arise. This does not necessarily mean that the plant is more poisonous when dried than in the green state but that grazing animals have more opportunity to avoid eating it when at pasture than when it is included in hay. Statements have been made at various times that hay containing horsetail is safe for animal feeding after it has been in the stack for over six months. The author cannot subscribe to this view because he has known hay containing a large proportion of *E. arvense*, which poisoned horses and sheep during one autumn, also poisoned bullocks in the autumn of the following year; it had then been in the stack for not less than sixteen months.

Mature plants contain a large amount of silica, which makes them extemely hard when dried; so harsh and hard in fact that they have been used by generations of country people as pot-scourers. Silica is not poisonous and young plants, which contain very little of it, are apparently more poisonous than older ones. An alkaloid, palustrine, has been extracted from marsh horsetail (*E. palustre*) but little is known of its action on the animal body. It has also been shown that an enzyme, thiaminase, which is capable of destroying vitamin B_1, is present in horsetail as well as in bracken and there is good evidence in support of the view that this agent is responsible for the symptoms shown by horses in particular, when suffering from poisoning by either horsetail or bracken which, in the case of both plants, results in a vitamin B_1 deficiency; the symptoms are identical, it has been reproduced experimentally and horses poisoned by either plant respond favourably to treatment with aneurin (vitamin B_1).

In horses, the symptoms of horsetail or of bracken poisoning may pass unnoticed during the very early stages. There is progressive loss of condition, a generally unthrifty appearance and slow pulse; the appetite remains fairly good. Later, they lose their rotund bellies, become tucked up and hollow in the flanks; the muscles of the hind-quarters begin to waste, particularly those on the outer sides, giving the flanks a still more hollow appearance. The gait becomes unsteady, the animal reels as it walks and may have difficulty in turning. By this time, the pulse is fast and weak and even light exercise causes trembling and exhaustion. In extreme cases, horses which lie down may be unable to rise without assistance.

Sheep and cattle are also affected by hay containing horsetail and, in recent years, this form of poisoning has become relatively more common among dairy herds. The most marked symptoms are a rapid and spectacular fall in milk yield in conjunction with serious loss of condition. Diarrhoea is commonly, but not always, present.

Treatment. Change of diet is the first essential. The administration of vitamin B_1, good nursing, quietude and a generous diet will usually effect rapid improvement, provided treatment is instituted early.

For further reading

ALKALOID OF E. PALUSTRE

E. GLET, J. GUTSCHMIDT and P. GLET, 1936, *Hoppe-Seyl. Z.* **244.** 229–43.

CHEMISTRY OF EQUISETUM SPP.

Sci. Libr. Bibliogr. Ser. Lond. **404.**

Horses

I. A. GUAYNIM, 1943, *Veterinariya, Moscow,* (3) 73–5. (Summary in French).
J. ST. GEORGES, 1943, *Rev. Oka* **17.** 220–1.
S. FORENBACHER, 1948, *Vet. Arhiv.* **18.** 9/10. 193–6. (Summary in English.)
E. T. R. EVANS, W. C. EVANS, and H. E. ROBERTS, 1951, *Brit. Vet. J.* **107.** 364–71, 399–411.

FILICALES

The Ferns are very well distributed in Britain, and although there may be a few which are poisonous if eaten in quantity, poisoning by them is not recognized, except in the case of Bracken (*Pteridium aquilinum* (L.) Kuhn) and perhaps the Male Fern (*Dryopteris filix-mas* (L.) Schott).

The author can find no record of poisoning by the fresh or growing male fern, but as extracts of the rhizomes are used medicinally for the expulsion of tape-worms and flukes, and poisoning by overdosing with these medicaments does sometimes occur, the remote possibility of poisoning by the plant in its natural state is mentioned.

BRACKEN, Brake (*Pteridium aquilinum* (L.) Kuhn. syn. *Pteris aquilina* L.)

Bracken is, by far, the commonest British fern. It is to be found on dry heaths, commons, hillsides and in hedgerows in all parts of the country. It is a stout, stiff, erect plant which may, according to the poverty or fertility of the soil, attain a height of 1–2 feet (30–60 cm.) or grow to be as tall as a man. It is a perennial with a hard, creeping rhizome which may creep for long distances underground. The fronds were likened by the ancients to the wings of an eagle and from this it derived its Latin name. Spores take the place of seeds and these are to be found in tiny spore cases, arranged in linear clusters called sori, on the underside of the fronds. The whole plant dies down to ground level in the autumn and new growth appears again from the rhizome in spring. It is said that lime deficiency, rabbits and grazing the land with sheep, all encourage its growth and spread but there is little concrete evidence to show that any or all of them make a significant difference.

Bracken is poisonous while green and remains poisonous if cut in the green state, dried and stacked. For this reason, it is not customary to harvest it for bedding animals until late in the season, when the sori are ripe and the fronds turning brown. Young bracken is known to contain harmless amounts of hydrocyanic acid, and tannic acid has been found in the fronds and stems of mature plants, but neither of these substances can be held responsible for the symptoms shown by poisoned animals. Bracken has also been shown to contain thiaminase, an enzyme capable of destroying vitamin B_1, and there can be little doubt that this is the agent responsible for the symptoms shown by horses suffering from bracken poisoning, which in these animals is essentially typical of vitamin B_1 deficiency and is clinically indistinguishable—by symptoms or response to treatment—from the vitamin B_1 deficiency which occurs when horses are poisoned by horsetail (see page 25). Bracken poisoning is well recognized among horses in Wales and in many other parts of the world; it has been reported to have occurred in pigs in Britain, but its occurrence in these animals must be very rare. Although it has been reported in sheep in New Zealand, any occurrence of the disease in British sheep under natural conditions has generally passed unrecognized until Parker and McCrea (1965) reported bracken poisoning in sheep on North Yorkshire moors. The syndrome they described was very similar to the haemorrhagic conditions seen in bracken poisoning of cattle and diagnosis was supported by ante-mortem blood counts. Sheep were seen to eat bracken during July and August and losses were heaviest from August to October.

Bracken poisoning of cattle is well known in all parts of the world. It is not a simple vitamin B_1 deficiency as in the horse, but something much more complex. (It must be remembered that while the horse, with its simple stomach, is dependent upon the vitamin content of its food for its normal requirement of vitamin B_1, cattle—through the action of the micro-organisms which inhabit their rumens—are able to synthesize more than sufficient for their needs.) The disease occurs sporadically during late summer and autumn, chiefly among yearlings and young adult stock, although occasionally calves and milking cows, bedded upon dried bracken, may become affected during winter. The ingestion of bracken by cattle over a long period results in damage to the bone marrow, with consequent interference with blood clotting and a serious reduction in the number of white blood corpuscles, which may virtually disappear from the blood. The high temperature and invasion of the blood stream by bacteria which occur during the late stages of the disease may not be unconnected with this diminution in the numbers of white corpuscles.

The early symptoms in calves are loss of appetite, and a watery discharge from the eyes and nostrils. Swellings of the throat commonly cause difficulty in breathing and, as a consequence, an affected calf makes a roaring sound. There is high temperature, and death occurs in from three to five days after the onset of symptoms.

In older cattle, the early symptoms are lack of appetite, refusal of food and water, and a slight watery discharge from the eyes and nostrils; there is often a slight drip of watery saliva from the mouth. Rumination ceases and, if out of doors, the affected animal stands or lies apart from the others. The temperature may be raised by one or two degrees, and the pulse is weak. Later, the discharges become blood-tinged, respiration becomes laboured, and the muzzle dry and inclined to be scaly around the nostrils. At first the faeces are small, dark coloured, firm and slightly drier than usual, but as the condition of the animal deteriorates, enteritis supervenes and blood is passed in clots or mixed with the faeces. Urine is at first dark coloured and later may contain blood and haemoglobin. Passage of urine ceases altogether in the last stages of the disease and this, coupled with a sharp rise in temperature up to 107–108°F, indicates the invasion of the blood stream by bacteria. Death usually occurs on about the third or fourth day of the illness.

The post-mortem picture seen in horses dead of bracken poisoning is not characteristic, but is consistent with death from heart failure.

Post-mortem examination of calves reveals an excess of fluid in the region of the throat and neck and, on occasion, between the muscles of the legs. Although minute haemorrhages may be found in many parts of the body they are not such a feature of the disease as in older animals.

Post-mortem examination of older cattle reveals petechial and massive haemorrhages under the skin, under both visceral and parietal peritoneum; particularly on the outer walls of the rumen and the abdominal surface of the diaphragm, under the pleura, in the heart muscle and in the kidneys. Ulcers of varying size, from which severe haemorrhages have occurred, are usually found on the inner walls of the intestine, and often in the abomasum or fourth stomach.

Treatment. When compared with the high measure of success which attends treatment with vitamin B_1 of bracken poisoning in horses, any treatment of the disease in cattle is extremely disappointing. Under both experimental and natural conditions, the administration of vitamin B_1, and of a wide range of other likely vitamins besides, has proved to be of no value. It has been stated that the administration of batyl alcohol, alone or in conjunction with antibiotics, in the hope of increasing the activity of bone marrow and of preventing bacterial invasion, may prove of value in the early stages but, in many reported instances, this, too, has proved ineffective. Until there is some major breakthrough and a totally new form of treatment is evolved, it may safely be said that any ruminant which shows acute symptoms of bracken poisoning has an extremely slight chance of recovery.

It is only reasonable to suspect that the companions of poisoned animals have also eaten bracken and, although they may not show visible clinical symptoms, that blood changes associated with the disease may have commenced. They should, therefore, be removed from any further access to the plant and be fed liberally on a diet rich in protein, some of which should be of animal origin. Blood examinations, leucocyte or platelet counts and tests for clotting power may be considered worth while in any attempt to pick out likely victims in the early stages.

The presence of a carcinogen has been demonstrated in bracken by Evans and Mason (1965) who, in a carefully controlled experiment, fed 40 rats on a diet which contained 34 per cent of dried bracken fronds. They reported, nearly a year after the investigation commenced, that 20 males and 14 females had died or been killed in poor condition. Varying in degree, all of them suffered from cancerous tumours of the small intestine, chiefly in the ileal region, which were confirmed as adenocarcinoma of the mucosa. One female rat developed a mammary tumour. An equivalent number of control rats, kept under the same environmental conditions except for the bracken, remained alive and healthy throughout. In order to eliminate any effect which might have been exerted by thiaminase both experimental and control rats were given extra-dietary vitamin B_1 by injection. They state that in a private communication, Parker and McCrea said that they had encountered the same type of tumour in older sheep which had died on bracken-infested North Yorkshire Moors.

For further reading

CATTLE

W. C. Evans, 1964, *Vet. Rec.* **76.** 365–72.

SHEEP

W. H. Parker and C. T. McCrea, 1965, *Vet. Rec.* **77.** 861–6.

CARCINOGENIC ACTIVITY

I. A. Evans and J. Mason, 1965, *Nature Lond.* **208.** 913–4.

Gymnosperms

CONIFERAE

Britain is rich in coniferous trees, numerous exotic species and varieties supplementing our native species. They can be seen everywhere. Few of them can be considered poisonous, although they contain resins and essential oils which, if taken in large quantities, would cause inflammation of the alimentary tract and the kidneys. Animals are not attracted to most of them; their aromatic odour and unpleasant taste prevent them from eating sufficient to cause any harm. The Juniper tree (*Juniperus communis*, L.) has caused gastro-enteritis and blood-stained urine when eaten by a goat, and two species of Cupressus are believed to have been the cause of death of cattle in a similar manner. McDonald (1956) in New Zealand, suspected *Cupressus macrocarpa* Hartw. ex Gord. of being the cause of a severe illness which affected nine cows. They aborted and retained their placentae. Two died and the remainder recovered after antihistaminic treatment.

In Britain cases are so rarely recorded, and the opportunities for poisoning by them are so many, that it is safe to say that although poisoning by them is possible, it is very highly improbable.

One genus, *Taxus*, however, is an exception to all the rules; yew trees are without doubt the most poisonous of our native trees or shrubs.

TAXACEAE

YEW, Common Yew (*Taxus baccata* L.) (Plate VII) and Irish Yew (*Taxus baccata* var. *fastigiata* Loud.)

The Yew is not a tall tree; even old specimens are seldom as tall as twenty feet. It can attain a great age, however, and the trunk may become very thick. It is found wild in southern England on the chalky downs, but there are few other places in Britain where it is not planted as an ornamental tree. The closeness of its evergreen foliage and its branching habit have made it a suitable subject for the art of topiary and for ornamental hedges.

Wood from yew is hard and tough and it was used for making long bows. Under many old statutes and enactments it was necessary for every parish to maintain yew trees from which archers could cut their bow staves. Because their poisonous properties were well known in those days of common grazings and few if any fences, they were planted and cared for in the churchyards, the only obvious place in which they were safely away from animals or children.

The branches of the common yew spread more or less horizontally from the trunk, while those of the Irish variety are more upright or erect. The leaves are inserted all round the stems, but they spread in one plane in two opposite ranks. They are very narrow and about a half to three-quarters of an inch long, shiny, and slightly convex on the upper side. Yew is generally dioecious; the male and female flowers are borne on separate trees. The flowers are small and inconspicuous; they may be found in the leaf axils in spring. The seed is only partially surrounded by the aril, which takes the form of a brilliant red, fleshy, translucent cup. The cup is attractive to children, and although the juicy part is sweet and not very poisonous, the seed it contains is deadly.

All parts of the tree are poisonous to man and to all classes of livestock. Taxine, the poisonous alkaloid contained in all parts, is a complex, chemical substance and is responsible for the sudden death which occurs in yew poisoning of all animals. It is rapidly absorbed from the alimentary tract and causes cessation of the heart's action. A trace of hydrocyanic acid, the alkaloid, ephedrine, and a volatile oil are also present. It is believed that the volatile oil is the cause of the intense irritation of the stomach, evidence of which is seen at the post-mortem examinations of animals where the time between eating the plant and death has been prolonged. Drying and storage do not lessen the toxicity of twigs and leaves, so that old dry clippings and fallen leaves are as poisonous to animals as the fresh plant.

Human cases of poisoning by yew are not common, the toxicity of the tree is well known and people avoid it and warn their children against the pretty fruits. Deaths have occurred among lunatics who have chewed the leaves and among women who have taken a decoction of the leaves, medicinally. Children have died from eating the cups. The symptoms and post-mortem findings of human cases are in every respect similar to those observed in animals.

Yew is one of the very few poisonous plants which animals will eat voluntarily at all times of the year, and it is not necessary for them to be hungry before they do so. The majority of cases of poisoning are the result of animals straying from pastures into gardens or churchyards, or through carelessness in the disposal of clippings and leaves.

Occasionally the animals reach overhanging branches from gardens or shrubberies, and in this connection there is the legal aspect to be considered. It has already been decided by the courts that where yew overhangs a neighbour's boundary and injures his stock, the owner of the yew is liable in damages.

The commonest symptom of yew poisoning is sudden death. If other symptoms are shown, death follows with remarkable rapidity, usually within five minutes in what appears to be a convulsion. The time which may elapse between the ingestion of the plant and death is very variable. Death may occur within a matter of minutes; it is not uncommon to find animals dead under the trees, with twigs and leaves in their mouths. In cattle, death may be delayed for as long as two days, the animal appearing normal in every way in the meanwhile. This difference in time is understandable when it is realized that the plant must be in proximity to, or in contact with, the stomach wall for the alkaloid to be absorbed into the blood; if it is mixed with other material, the time may be prolonged.

It is sometimes possible to save the lives of cattle known to have eaten yew by performing the operation of rumenotomy, removing all the stomach contents and replacing them with other foodstuffs. It must be remembered, however, that the animal is just as likely to die during the operation as at any other time, and pre-operative preparations should be made with this contingency in mind.

In those instances where a few animals have died out of a number which have all had access to yew, it is not uncommon for one or more of the living ones, after about sixteen hours, to show symptoms of abdominal pain and diarrhoea. They suffer from an acute gastro-enteritis which clears up in two or three days, after suitable treatment. It is extremely difficult in these cases to determine whether the symptoms are those of sub-lethal yew poisoning or of poisoning by other irritant plants, because wherever yew is growing, there is usually other toxic vegetation in the vicinity. Diagnosis cannot be confirmed or negatived in these cases by laboratory tests of the body fluids or excreta.

Post-mortem diagnosis is dependent upon finding leaves or twigs in the stomach. Where death has followed rapidly after ingestion, there is little or no inflammation, but should there have been a lapse of several hours between eating the plant and death, then inflammation of the stomach wall may be intense. The heart's action is arrested by taxine. The right side is usually flaccid, dark-coloured and filled with black, tarry blood. The left side is contracted and empty.

Prevention of yew poisoning is a matter of keeping gates closed and fences in repair. Clippings, and sweepings from under trees, as well as old twigs from wreaths or decorations, should be gathered together and burned.

For further reading

CUPRESSUS MACROCARPA

J. MacDonald, 1956, *N.Z. Vet. J.* **4.** 30.

YEW

M. Ratchoff, 1936, *Vet. Sbir.* **40.** 128–9.
J. W. H. Masheter, 1937, *Vet. Rec.* **49.** 265–6.

Sheep

R. Benoit, 1939, *Schweiz. Arch. Tierheilk.* **81.** 401–3. (In French).

Cattle

H. Linsert, 1942, *Tierärztl. Rdsch.* **48.** 319.
H. Doyle, 1942, *N.Z. J. Agric.* **65.** 287–8.
P. Cathelineau, (1950) *Bull. Acad. vét. Fr.* **23.** 116–20.
G. Eaton, 1941, *Vet. Rec.* **53.** 145–6.

Angiosperms

DICOTYLEDONS

RANUNCULACEAE

THE *Ranunculus* family includes many of the best known of our wild flowers, and the majority of them are poisonous if eaten in their fresh state. Traveller's Joy (*Clematis*), Pheasant's Eye (*Adonis*), Buttercups or Crowfoots (*Ranunculus*), Marsh Marigold (*Caltha*), the Hellebores (*Helleborus*), Columbine (*Aquilegia*), Monkshood or Aconite (*Aconitum*), and Baneberry (*Actaea*), are all known to have caused severe illness and deaths among animals. Most of them are rejected by grazing animals because of their acrid taste, and would appear to be eaten only during times of dire necessity, or by young animals turned out to graze for the first time.

Monkshood or aconite is believed by many writers to be Britain's most poisonous plant, but delphiniums and buttercups probably claim more victims, because their properties are less well known, and little care is taken to guard against their being eaten. Buttercups grow almost everywhere, and in one Surrey field the author has counted five species flowering at the same time.

MARSH MARIGOLD or King Cup (*Caltha palustris* L.)

The Marsh Marigold is a herbaceous perennial. It forms large tufts and, as its name implies, is found abundantly in wet meadows and marshes throughout Britain. The stems are annual and hollow. Most of the leaves grow from the rootstock on long stalks. They are usually round or kidney-shaped with crenated margins, and the stem leaves appear to clasp the stem. There are no petals, but five or six golden yellow sepals take their place in the flowers, which are seen during spring or early summer.

ANEMONES or Windflowers (*Anemone*)

The dull violet or purple-coloured Pasque Flower (*Anemone pulsatilla* L.) and the white or slightly pink Wood Anemone (*A. nemorosa* L.) are the native wild representatives of this genus, but two other species of wood anemone, the blue-flowered *A. apennina* L. and the yellow-flowered *A. ranunculoides* L., have become naturalized in some of our woodlands. The less common of the the two native species is the pasque flower, which is found only in a few parts of England, but not in Wales, Scotland, or Ireland. The wood anemones are found throughout Britain and are among the best known of the earlier spring flowers. The rootstock is perennial, and from it grow the leaves and flower-stalks. The flower-stems are quite naked except for a whorl of three leaves, which are placed around them, usually at a distance from the flower. These three leaves may, because they are divided, appear to be numerous, but only three will be found if they are carefully examined at the base, and they are characteristic of the genus. There are no petals, the colour of the flowers being in the sepals, of which there are usually six. The carpels are single-seeded; in the wood anemones the point is as long as the carpel itself, but in he pasque flower they have long feathery awns.

Animals may eat anemones during early spring when other green foods are scarce. Their poisonous principle is proto-anemonin, and the symptoms of poisoning are similar to those of the buttercups and other members of this family.

TRAVELLER'S JOY, Old Man's Beard (*Clematis vitalba* L.)

Traveller's Joy is the only climbing member of this family which grows wild in Britain and is found in hedgerows and woodlands in the southern half of the country. The stem is woody at its base; it may grow to the thickness of a man's wrist and several yards long. The leaves are pinnate, usually with five ovate, stalked leaflets. The flowers have four greenish-white sepals and no petals, they are in loose panicles on short axillary branches. The fruits form a dense white hairy mass, resembling a long silky beard, from which it takes one of its popular names.

All parts of the plant are poisonous, the active principle resembling proto-anemonin. It is a severe irritant and the juice, if applied to the skin, causes blistering. If eaten it causes enteritis and severe abdominal pain with diarrhoea, which in the end may be fatal. Poisoning by traveller's joy is rare, because of its acrid taste and the severe irritation it causes to the mouths of animals; they may bite it but seldom swallow it.

MEADOW RUE (*Thalictrum*)

Meadow Rue is mentioned only because members of this genus have caused poisoning in other countries. No cases have been recorded in Britain, where the plant is not common. The only species likely to occur in fodder is *T. flavum*, the Meadow Rue, which is not uncommon along ditches, rivers and streams north to Inverness and in Ireland. Various species are cultivated in gardens.

PHEASANT'S EYE (*Adonis annua* L.)

Pheasant's Eye is one of the uncommon members of the *Ranunculus* family and appears only occasionally in the warmer counties of southern England and sometimes in Scotland. It is an erect annual from 8–12 inches high with five to eight scarlet petals each with a dark spot at the base. It is reputed to have caused poisoning of pigs in southern Russia, which died after having shown symptoms of acute diarrhoea and heart failure. The poisonous principle is proto-anemonin. The name 'Pheasant's Eye' should not be confused with that of the Pheasant's Eye narcissus, which belongs to the *Amaryllis* family.

BUTTERCUPS AND CROWFOOTS (*Ranunculus*)

All the poisonous species in this genus have yellow flowers and are well known to the majority of readers.

LESSER CELANDINE, Pilewort (*Ranunculus ficaria* L.)

The Lesser Celandine is the earliest flowering of the *Ranunculi*. It is to be found in moist places almost everywhere in Britain, except in parts of the Western Highlands of Scotland. The flowers are single on the stems and stand about 6 inches high. They have three sepals and eight or nine oblong, glossy petals. The leaves are heart-shaped and shiny, and are darkish green in colour. Like the anemones, the lesser celandine is green and flowering in the very early spring; it is known to have poisoned sheep and cattle.

LESSER SPEARWORT (*R. flammula* L.)

The Lesser Spearwort is a common plant of wet pastures and marshes and is found throughout Britain. It is a glabrous annual or a perennial, seldom more than a foot high, with stems rooting and decumbent at the base. The lowest leaves may be ovate, but those above are lanceolate or linear; they may show slight toothing but they are otherwise entire. The very small (seldom more than half an inch in diameter) flowers, seen during the summer months, are carried on long peduncles. Horses and cattle have been poisoned by it.

GREAT SPEARWORT (*R. lingua* L.)

The Great Spearwort is not common in Britain, but may sometimes be found in wet places. It is a perennial, with a large mass of fibrous roots. The bright yellow flowers, over 1 inch in diameter, stand on erect hollow stems, 2–3 feet high, and the leaves are long, shining and lanceolate.

CELERY-LEAVED BUTTERCUP or Crowfoot (*R. sceleratus* L.)

The Celery-leaved Buttercup is an annual, and another inhabitant of damp places. It is found by the sides of ponds, watercourses, and in ditches. The dark green lower leaves are shiny and luxuriant in growth, compared with the other species, and are broadly lobed and crenate. The flowers are small and numerous with pale yellow petals scarcely longer than the calyx. The flowering stems may attain a height of 2 feet. The carpels are very small in an ovate head which becomes more oblong as the fruits ripen.

The celery-leaved buttercup has the reputation of being the most poisonous of all the buttercups. This is probably due more to its luxuriance than to its greater poison content. In suitable conditions it may cover comparatively large areas of ground, with a dense mass of foliage up to a foot high which smothers the less vigorous plants around it. It can be easily realized that a much larger amount of this plant can be eaten in a shorter time than of those species with less foliage, or of plants which are scattered.

COMMON BUTTERCUP or Crowfoot (*R. acris* L.)

The Common Buttercup is found in almost every pasture, and is a soft hairy perennial. Its height depends much upon the nature of the soil; on poor land it may be only 6 inches but on a good soil it may grow as high as 3 feet. The stems are erect and carry the large, bright yellow flowers in loose cymes. The sepals are yellowish-green and shorter than the petals; they are concave and spread out horizontally, but are not reflected back towards the peduncle. Nearly all the leaves arise from the stems, they are stalked, and are divided into three, five, or seven segments, which are again divided into three toothed lobes. The plant flowers from early summer until late autumn, and the carpels are in a shiny globular head.

CREEPING BUTTERCUP (*R. repens* L.)

The Creeping Buttercup has flowers and fruits similar to those of the common buttercup (*q.v.*), but it is easily distinguished from it by the runners which shoot from among the radical leaves. The runners root from nodes and rapidly form new plants. The flower-stalks are grooved and seldom more than a foot high. The leaves, which are divided into three segments, each with a stalk, have a more ovate appearance than those of the common buttercup. This is one of the most troublesome weeds to eradicate from pastures and cornfields.

BULBOUS BUTTERCUP, St. Anthony's Turnip (*R. bulbosus* L.)

The Bulbous Buttercup, the small buttercup of lawns and pastures, is seldom more than a foot high, often less. The stem is swollen at its base, forming a bulb below ground. The flowers and fruits resemble those of the common buttercup while the leaves are more like those of the creeping buttercup (*q.v.*).

POISONING BY PROTO-ANEMONIN

All the members of the *Ranunculus* family so far described, together with some of those species which are cultivated in gardens, and probably the Globe Flowers (*Trollius*), contain an irritant poisonous substance, proto-anemonin, which is a yellow volatile oil. It is present in its greatest concentration during the flowering period. It is not a stable compound and on standing or storing for a short time it precipitates non-poisonous crystals or flakes of anemonin. Farmers have known for many generations that hay containing large quantities of buttercups is quite harmless. Had the animals eaten the same crop in its green state, they would have been severely ill or perhaps even have died. Poisoning by buttercups is rare among grazing animals, because even though the plants abound in pastures and spread very rapidly, their acrid burning taste makes them repulsive. They are rejected except during very dry seasons when pastures are bare and the hungry creatures graze the greener and more luxuriant growths around the ditches and pond edges. This is another reason why the celery-leaved buttercup is considered to be the most poisonous of them all. Poisoning is sometimes seen in housed animals which are fed on grass freshly cut from meadows, which contains large amounts of buttercups. Young cattle turned out for the first time may gorge them and be ill as the result. As with many other plants, an animal which has been once poisoned and has acquired the taste for buttercups, will often, as soon as recovery is complete, go back and eat more of them with similar ill-effects. The author saw two heifers, which had recovered from acute poisoning with celery-leaved buttercup, on their first day out to graze immediately go back to the same place in the field and start to eat them again. However many times they were chased away they returned and, eventually, for their safety, were removed from that pasture altogether.

The early symptoms of poisoning by any of these plants are colic, salivation and inflammation of the lining membranes of the mouth which may be so severe as even to cause blisters. Fiery reddening is seen in the mouths of horses, goats and pigs, but the harder membranes of cattle do not show it quite so distinctly. The author saw severe blistering in the mouths of housed goats which had been fed with freshly gathered *R. sceleratus* and *R. acris* 'to improve the colour of their milk'—an old and dangerous fallacy; it resulted in the death of one and the severe illness of two others. In the later stages there is dark coloured, almost black, diarrhoea, and blood-stained urine. By the time these symptoms occur the gait is unsteady, particularly of the hind legs. The animals often appear to have impaired vision or may be quite blind. Death usually occurs in a convulsion or fit.

Post-mortem appearances show little which is definite, except the presence of pieces of plant in the stomach. There is inflammation of the whole of the alimentary tract, especially marked in the small intestine. Chemical analysis of the stomach contents will do little to confirm or negative the presence of the poison.

Only one fatal case in children has been recorded, but the author has seen on two separate occasions children who, in digging for pignuts (*Conopodium majus*) had found and chewed the bulbous roots of *R. bulbosus* in mistake. Vomiting was almost immediate and persisted only for a short time. After that they were apparently none the worse. It appeared that the irritant substances were thrown back before they had time to do serious harm.

First-aid treatment. Administer raw eggs and sugar, in skimmed milk, to allay the severe irritation of the mouth and stomach as early as possible. Further treatment should be prescribed only by the medical practitioner or veterinary surgeon.

HELLEBORES (*Helleborus* spp.)

The Hellebores are perennials, of which two species, the Stinking Hellebore or Setterwort (*H. foetidus* L.) and the Green Hellebore or Bear's-foot (*H. viridis* L.) are natives of England. They are found in the southern counties, on chalk or limestone soils. A third species, which is perhaps more widely known because of its cultivation in gardens throughout the country, is the Christmas Rose or Black Hellebore (*H. niger* L.), which has been introduced here from south-eastern Europe. The leaves of hellebores are of a lighter green colour and more rigid than those of most members of the *Ranunculus* family. The flowers, which appear in late winter or early spring, have five large sepals which are often mistaken for the petals. These latter, of which there are usually eight or ten, are very tiny and tubular in shape.

GREEN HELLEBORE has two radical leaves divided into seven to eleven oblong, toothed, segments which are 3 or 4 inches long; the central ones are free, while those on either side are connected together at the base, giving the leaf the appearance from which the name 'Bear's-foot' was derived. The flower-stem, hardly longer than the leaves, bears two or three drooping flowers yellowish-green in colour when widely open.

STINKING HELLEBORE or Setterwort (Plate II) forms a thicker tuft than the green hellebore. The stem leaves are stiffer and more shining, and the segments narrower and less toothed. The radical leaves are withered at the time of flowering. The sepals which are pale green, and tinged with a dull purple, overlap each other to give the flowers a globular form. They droop in a close panicle from a stem over a foot high, hanging their heads as if ashamed of the vile and foetid odour they emit.

CHRISTMAS ROSE has a white or whitish-pink flower, and leaves which are more deeply toothed, of a coarser texture, and a darker green colour, than those of the other two species. It is not particular about soil and is cultivated in gardens almost everywhere in Britain.

All parts of the hellebores are poisonous to men and animals. Formerly they were collected and used in the form of a tincture as a remedy for worms, and an infusion of the stinking hellebore was used as a dressing for lice. Owing to their poisonous properties and the number of deaths which followed their use, they have long been abandoned in favour of safer and more effective remedies. Cases of poisoning by them still occur, however, usually as the result of animals having access to garden refuse, or during severe weather when these plants are green at a time when little else is. The poisonous principles are two glycosides, helleborein and helleborin, which are persistent in the plant after drying and storage. Only prolonged boiling will reduce their toxicity.

Symptoms likely to be observed in cattle and sheep are: acute dark-coloured diarrhoea containing blood and mucus; the abdomen is tense, and violent intermittent straining alternates with quiet periods; urination is excessive and frequent, and the pulse is intermittent. Heifers which died in Italy after a dressing of a hellebore preparation had been applied for parasites, showed symptoms similar to those mentioned above as well as an acute inflammation of the skin. It was believed that they had licked off the dressing in an attempt to ease the skin irritation. The poisons have been detected in all parts of the body of poisoned animals, and it is recorded that persons drinking milk from poisoned cows have themselves been affected by acute diarrhoea and vomiting.

First-aid treatment should consist of administering eggs, sugar and milk, in an attempt to allay the irritant action on the stomach and bowel-walls, until professional advice can be obtained. There is no specific antidote.

ACONITUM spp. Monkshood, Wolf's-bane or Aconite

Monkshoods are perennial herbaceous plants with stout, black, taproot-like rootstocks and much divided leaves. The popular name is taken from the dark blue helmet-shaped flowers which form a dense raceme on a stem from 18 inches to 3 feet high (45–100 cm.). The native British species, *Aconitum anglicum* Stapf., is found growing wild on river banks and in moist shady places in western counties of England and in South Wales. The cultivated forms, which mostly belong to the aggregate of *A. napellus* L. and their hybrids, are to be found in moist and shaded herbaceous borders throughout the country and are equally as toxic as the wild plant. Monkshood is said by many to be the most dangerous of all British plants and all parts of it are poisonous.

The roots, which are collected in the autumn and dried, are used in the preparation of medicinal tinctures and liniments. The poisonous principle is chiefly aconitine, one of the narcotic alkaloids which slow the action of the heart; there are also other, less important alkaloids. Since very early times aconite has been used for the purpose of easing pain, both internally and externally, but because of the uncertainty of its poison content and the difficulty of standardizing the products, its use is yearly becoming more limited and is fast being replaced by more reliable drugs.

Because its toxic properties are so well known, poisoning by the wild plant is rare, but it may occur if roots are thrown out of gardens and shrubberies. Every care must be taken in places where it is cultivated to see that animals do not gain access to it, as the poison persists after any parts, stems, leaves, or roots have been cut and dried.

Cases of fatal poisoning of human beings have been recorded where the root has been used in mistake for horse-radish.

Symptoms shown are a slowing of the breathing and heart rate, with weakening of the pulse. In the horse there are spasmodic attempts at vomiting with the regurgitation of a frothy mucus, intense colic, followed by paralysis, dilated pupils, and death from asphyxia. Two cows, seen by the author, which had eaten large quantities of delphinium and monkshood, thrown out from a garden in the autumn, showed little evidence of pain; they were down and unable to rise, the skin was cold, the pupils dilated and the breathing and pulse were almost imperceptible. An attempt by the attendant to drench one of them ended fatally. The cow made no effort to swallow and was suffocated by the medicament. Stimulant treatment by injection had little effect on the other, and she died about five hours after eating the plant. Post-mortem examination showed very little evidence of inflammatory changes in the stomach and bowel. Changes in the lungs and heart were similar to those of suffocation, in both animals. From the amount of the plants found in the stomachs, it was estimated that neither animal could have eaten less than twelve pounds.

First-aid treatment cannot be specific; warmth, stimulants, and frictional rubbing of the skin, are indicated in an attempt to assist the blood circulation.

AQUILEGIA, Columbine (*Aquilegia vulgaris* L.)

The Columbine is found in woods and shaded places as far north as southern Scotland. It is a perennial herb with long stalked leaves, mostly radical, which are divided into three segments, each of which is three-lobed with crenated edges. The leaves form a tuft at the base of the plant. The stem, which grows to a height of 1½–2 feet, bears a loose panicle of flowers with a few leaves at its extremities. The flowers are dark blue or purple in colour; they have five sepals and five petals, each of which terminates in a horn-shaped spur. They are not likely to be eaten in any quantity, but Cornevin (1893) points out that their poisonous properties are similar to those of aconite, and that an infusion of the seeds, used medicinally in several countries, is dangerous to children.

DELPHINIUM spp. Larkspur

All species in the genus Delphinium are poisonous. In Britain, *Delphinium ambiguum* L., a weed once common in the cornfields of the eastern counties, is an erect annual which grows from 1–2 feet (30–60 cm.) high. The flowers may be red, white or blue and the calyx, which is also coloured, terminates in a spur. *D. orientale* Gay, the annual larkspur commonly cultivated in gardens, and the perennial 'delphiniums' which are mostly hybrids, are all equally toxic. They contain alkaloids of which ajacine and ajaconine are the most important and which give rise to symptoms similar to those caused by the alkaloids of aconite. The seeds of a European species *D. staphisagria* L. Stavesacre, were for long used in the preparation of dressings for lice and fleas.

The likelihood of poisoning by the wild growing plant in Britain is remote unless it has been included in hay or straw. On the other hand, every care must be taken to prevent animals, particularly cattle, from having access to cultivated annual or perennial larkspurs and delphiniums, either while growing or when thrown out from gardens in the autumn. In America, where larkspurs are considered to be the most noxious plants of the Western Ranges, it is said that cattle will eat them at any time, whether hungry or not, and that half a pound per hundred pounds live weight is sufficient to cause death.

ACTAEA, Herb Christopher, Baneberry (*Actaea spicata* L.)

Herb Christopher is found only in the northern counties of England, and even there it is quite local in distribution. The leaves (mostly radical) are large, and rather resemble those of the Elder, being divided and coarsely toothed. The stem is 1–2 feet high and the flowers are small and white on a loose terminal raceme. The small berries are nearly black in colour. As the name baneberry implies, it is poisonous when eaten and the symptoms it causes are gastro-enteritis, diarrhoea, vomiting, and delirium. Little is known of the active principle, which appears to be an essential oil.

For further reading

RANUNCULI

M. MIRCOVIC, 1936, *Jugosl. vet. Glasn.* **16.** 544–5.
G. D. SHEARER, 1938, *Vet. J.* **94.** 22–32.
O. V. GUNNING, 1949, *Brit. Vet. J.* **105.** No. 10. 393.

HELLEBORUS

L. BERSELLI, 1936, *Nuova Vet.* **14.** 197–8.

PAPAVERACEAE

The poisonous members of the poppy family are the Red Poppy (*Papaver rhoeas* L.), the Greater Celandine (*Chelidonium majus* L.), and to a less extent, the yellow Horned or Sea Poppy (*Glaucium flavum* Crantz). The White, or Opium, Poppy (*P. somniferum* L.) has been cultivated here and has established itself in a wild state in a few places in the eastern counties.

RED POPPY (*P. rhoeas* L.) and White or Opium Poppy (*P. somniferum* L.)

The red poppy is a common annual weed of cornfields—so well known that a description would be almost superfluous. The petals are gathered dried, and used in the manufacture of a medicinal syrup (Syrupus Rhoeados), which imparts a bitter flavour and red colour to the medicaments to which it is added.

Only if eaten in very large quantity is the red poppy poisonous to livestock, and it is usually obtained by them mixed with other fodder.

Although the active principle is rhoeadine, and the opium alkaloids are not present in the red poppy, the symptoms shown by cattle poisoned by it are similar to those after poisoning by opium and white poppy, except that the intestinal symptoms are more marked (Cornevin 1893.)

During the late war a revival of the cultivation of the white poppy took place in France, for the purpose of obtaining edible oil. The feeding of the residues to cattle resulted in many cases of poisoning. The symptoms were a marked gastro-enteritis, nervous excitement, lack of appetite and colicky pains. When moved, the animals appeared to have little control. There were few fatal cases but most of the survivors were an economic loss, lactation ceased, and they became generally unthrifty, progressively losing weight. The poisonous principles of opium—morphine and its associated alkaloids—are present in all parts of the plant, but most is found in the capsule and stems.

First-aid treatment consists, in the early stages, of keeping the patient quiet during the period of excitement, followed by the administration of purgatives and stimulants.

Members of the poppy genus which are recorded as having poisoned animals in other countries are the Long-headed Poppy (*P. dubium* L.), the Rough Poppy (*P. hybridum* L.) and the Iceland Poppy (*P. nudicaule* L.).

GREATER CELANDINE (*Chelidonium majus* L.) (Plate I)

The Greater Celandine is a perennial found in most parts of Britain. It thrives best near old walls and ruins, and is less common in Scotland than in England and Wales. All parts of the plant have an unpleasant foetid odour, and animals avoid it in its fresh state. The stems are thin, erect, and branching, they are slightly hairy and are filled with an evil-smelling, yellow juice, which turns red when exposed to the air. The thin leaves are covered with a pale fine bloom on the under-surface, and are divided and lobed. The flowers, which are seen during the whole summer, are small and yellow, and have two sepals and four petals; they are in a loose umbel, usually three or six together, on a long peduncle. The seeds are in a long, smooth, cylindrical, pod-like, capsule about 1½–2 inches long.

In olden times, the greater celandine was cultivated and gathered for its medicinal virtues. It was given to patients, both human and animal, to bring about what may be termed internal cleanliness. Those unfortunates to whom it was administered were well purged and vomited, and it did not require very much blood-letting to hasten their end. The author has on several occasions been called to attend both horses and cattle suffering from acute conjunctivitis, the result of having had their eyes bathed in an infusion of celandine flowers and stems, as a treatment for some minor condition. Externally, the juice was applied to warts, and was diluted as a skin wash for parasites. Since it is no longer used for these purposes, poisoning by it has become rare. The active principles are chelidonine, α homochelidonine, chelerythrine and sanguinarine.

The symptoms of poisoning according to Cornevin (1893) are those one would expect after the administration of a drastic purgative, but Reeks (1903) quoted by Lander, found cows showing drowsiness, salivation, great thirst, uncertain gait, torpid bowels and active kidneys. Death took place after two hours in a convulsion.

HORNED POPPY or Sea Poppy (*Glaucium flavum* Crantz, syn. *G. luteum* Scop.)

The Horned Poppy has large yellow flowers and thick rough leaves, which are very much divided. It is an annual which is found around the English coasts. No actual cases of poisoning by this plant in its wild state have been recorded. It is included here because it is known to contain the poisonous alkaloids; glaucine, protopine, chelerythrine, and sanguinarine. Should poisoning occur, the symptoms would be similar to those caused by the greater celandine.

For further reading

OPIUM POPPY

Rec. Méd. vét., 1946, **122.** 23–4, 310–3.

CRUCIFERAE

The family name of the crucifers means 'cross bearers' and is taken from the flowers in which the four petals are arranged in the form of a cross. The family includes many favourite garden flowers such as stocks, wallflowers and candytufts, as well as vegetables like cabbage, turnip, mustard, radishes, horse-radish and kale.

The main features of the poisonous members of this family are that they are all herbaceous. The earliest flowers appear as a corymb but as growth continues, it gradually lengthens into a raceme. The flowers have four petals and four sepals. The fruit is a specialized capsule, which is divided into two cells by a thin partition.

CHARLOCK, Kedlock, Wild Mustard (*Sinapis arvensis* L., syn. *Brassica sinapis* Vis.)

Charlock is an annual which is a common and harmful weed of cornfields. The leaves are rough and slightly hairy. The flowers are bright yellow and flowering continues for most of the summer; the pods have a beak which takes up about one-third of their length. The seeds are capable of remaining dormant in the ground for many years and germinate only when conditions are favourable. Selective weed-killers have been used more in the control of this weed than of any other.

There is a current belief among farmers that charlock is not poisonous until the pods have formed, which seems to be well substantiated in practice. Gallie and Paterson (1945) describe symptoms in lambs folded on a field of rape in which charlock was so abundant that it was impossible to grasp a plant of rape without taking one of charlock with it. The charlock pods were well formed. The symptoms were those of acute gastro-enteritis; abdominal pain, slight frothing around the mouth and nose, grunting and diarrhoea. Post-mortem examination revealed acute inflammation of the stomachs, bowels and kidneys. Horses have been reported to have been poisoned by charlock in Soviet Russia, and Kunicyn (1937) recommends camphor as an antidote.

WHITE MUSTARD (*Sinapis alba* L., syn. *Brassica alba* (L.) Boiss.)

White mustard is the cultivated mustard. It is grown as a green crop for sheep, and in gardens for salads. The stem grows between 1 and 2 feet in height and is usually covered with stiff hairs. The leaves are rough and lobed, and the flowers large and yellow. The pod, ¾–1 inch long, has a flat hairy beak which takes up over half of its total length and contains one seed at its base.

The author examined a flock of lambs in Kent which, because of salivation and inability to rise, were suspected to be suffering from foot-and-mouth disease. They had been folded for two days and nights on white mustard. Owing to movement restrictions in the district, the crop had been left ungrazed longer than was the usual practice and the pods had formed. During the second night there had been a severe frost. Five lambs were dead and about forty of the others were down and unable to rise. Others which could walk had symptoms of frothy salivation and a light green diarrhoea. The symptoms and post-mortem findings were almost identical with those of poisoning with charlock, as described by Gallie and Paterson. The animals were removed from the field, and those that could walk were fed on hay, while the remainder received the local mixture of eggs and whiting, given in milk.

Eaton (1941) found three bullocks dead in a field, folded on a white mustard stubble which had been previously grazed over by sheep. Post-mortem examination showed that the rumen was packed with coarse fibrous mustard stems, and the lining membrane was more easily detached than usual. The fourth stomach was inflamed, there was patchy inflammation of the small bowels, some lung inflammation, and there were no signs of a struggle at death.

WILD RADISH, White or Jointed Charlock (*Raphanus raphanistrum* L.)

Wild radish is an annual or a biennial, which is about 1–2 feet high, very branched, with divided or lobed rough leaves. The flowers are white or very pale lilac, with veined petals; sometimes they are pale yellow.

There are no records of poisoning by wild radish in recent British literature, but it has always been believed harmful to livestock if eaten in quantity. Trouche (1936) describes how fifty lambs in France were allowed to graze in a field covered with wild radish in an advanced stage of florescence. One died on the same night and five others were found dead next morning; others in the flock were unable to rise. Post-mortem examination made within two hours of death showed the rumen to be filled with the plant, the abdominal muscles were congested and the tissues yellow in colour. The heart and lungs were normal, the liver was friable, the kidneys congested and the bladder filled with blood-stained urine.

HORSE-RADISH (*Armoracia rusticana* Gaertn., syns. *A. lapathifolia* Gilib., *Cochlearia armoracia* L.)

Horse-radish is a perennial with a long tapering root, from which grow the leaves. The large leaves are rough to the touch but are not hairy; they are on long stalks and are undivided. They are toothed at the edges and are about 1 foot or more long and 4–6 inches broad. The stems are 2–3 feet high and bear tiny white flowers in a terminal panicle. The pods, even if they form, seldom ripen in the British climate. It is cultivated in gardens for culinary use, but it may be found wild in many parts of the country.

Horse-radish poisoning is not common because of the pungent taste of the leaves and roots, but cases have been recorded in Britain of poisoning of cattle, in which the symptoms were lowing and excitement followed by death from exhaustion and collapse. The author made post-mortem examinations of six ponies, which were found dead after having broken out of their pasture into an orchard in which horse-radish was growing in profusion. Large quantities of the leaves and flowering stems were found in the stomachs, which were acutely inflamed and smelt typically of horse-radish. There were no other lesions. The animals had obviously suffered acute pain before death. Two fattening pigs were found dead about three hours after being fed on uncooked hotel garbage. Post-mortem examination showed acute inflammation of the stomach walls, which even after washing in water smelt strongly of horse-radish. There were no other lesions. It was roughly estimated that these pigs had eaten two to three ounces of the grated root between them.

All the above members of this family owe their poisonous properties to volatile oils similar in type to oil of mustard. All of them are very strong irritants when allowed to come in contact with living tissues.

First-aid treatment consists of administering eggs and skimmed milk; preferably with sugar added. Constipation may follow the early stages of recovery and an oily purgative may be necessary.

KALE (*Brassica oleracea* L.)

The three main varieties of kale, marrowstem, thousand-headed and hungry-gap, like the various types of cabbage, broccoli, cauliflower, kohlrabi and brussels sprouts, have all been developed by selection and cultivation from wild cabbage species. Kale is a widely grown fodder plant in many parts of the world and wherever fed in excessive quantities it causes trouble. In Europe, it has long been considered to be one of the common causes of acute anaemia accompanied by haemoglobinuria and liver damage among cattle and sheep, particularly after the crop has been frosted.

Rosenberger (1939) reports from Germany that after feeding large quantities of marrowstem kale (80–112 lb per day) for a long period, either in the fresh state or ensiled, cattle suffered from an acute anaemia which was sufficient to cause death if the diet were not changed as soon as symptoms were noticed. The earliest symptom was usually haemoglobinuria or blood-stained urine, which appeared about the eighth or tenth day after kale feeding had begun. This was followed by anaemia, rapid loss of weight and staggering gait. The fertility of non-pregnant animals was considerably reduced, but those worst affected were the heavy milkers and cows in late pregnancy. Post-mortem examination revealed general anaemia, haemoglobinaemia, haemoglobinuria, slight jaundicing, haemolytic necrosis of the liver lobules and hyperaemia of the spleen. The heart muscle showed degeneration and there were petechiae (blood splashes) in the trachea and bronchi. Death was due to liver insufficiency. Rosenberger recommends that if marrowstem kale is to be fed over a long period, cattle should not receive more than 30 lb per day, although fattening animals may receive up to a maximum of 45 lb.

A somewhat similar syndrome was encountered by Dunbar and Chambers (1963) in two outbreaks of illness among cows which were fed upon frost damaged kale. Examination of blood from four of those affected revealed an inorganic phosphorus content of 1·7 to 3·8 mg per cent and smears, negative for babesia, showed punctate basophilia. The only one which died became paralysed and had convulsions prior to death and post-mortem examination showed extensive jaundicing of the carcase.

Kale, like other descendants of wild cabbage, contains one or more goitrogens of the thiouracil or thiocyanate type (see page 7) and, in England and New Zealand, it has been established as one of the main causes of congenital hypothyroidism or goitre of lambs and calves when fed to pregnant cows and ewes. Although the dams themselves may show little effect at the time, death of the foetus in utero and non-infectious abortion or still-birth at term are the common result. Developmental changes occur in those foetuses which survive, particularly in parts dependent upon full thyroid function, and even the thyroid itself shows the typical enlargement of goitre. Survival of the foetus must, obviously, depend upon the stage of gestation reached when kale feeding began and, if not too badly affected at birth, calves and lambs stand a reasonable chance of making a satisfactory recovery if suitable treatment with iodine is instituted early.

Outbreaks of this type of disease cause a complete upset of breeding programmes particularly in dairy herds where loss of milk yield following abortion and consequent infertility, often after full term parturition too, are usual sequelae.

The goitrogenicity of kale appears to vary from crop to crop and Allcroft and Salt (1961) carried out a series of experiments in an attempt to ascertain what factors might be involved. Their results showed that dressing of the ground with nitrogenous fertilizers caused an increase in goitrogenicity and kale grown on land dressed with Chilean nitrate of soda was more goitrogenic for rabbits than that grown on land to which ammonium sulphate or nitro-chalk had been applied. Conversely, the application of 24 lb of sodium iodate to the acre increased the iodine content of the kale, of the blood plasma and of the milk of a cow fed upon it and was sufficient to prevent goitrogenic effects upon pregnant rabbits and their young. They conclude that differences in manurial treatment, together with climatic variations, may be the possible explanation of the wide range of difference in goitrogenic potency of members of this species.

RAPE (*Brassica napus* L.)

Rape is grown extensively as a field crop throughout the world. In several parts it is grown mainly for its seed, from which rape or colza oil is obtained, and in other places it is used only as a fodder crop. Some of the 'mustard' which is sold in the early stage of its growth for salads is actually grown by a few market gardeners from rape seed; it is not so sharp to the palate as true mustard. In Great Britain, it is generally culivated for sheep, which are folded upon it and are seldom adversely affected by it. Cattle, if it is fed to them at all, are usually folded upon it early in the season while the plants are young and small.

Poisoning of cattle by rape is occasionally reported from every country where it is grown. The author's personal experience has been limited to the digestive and urinary types of the disease which have run a course similar to those described by Coté (1944) of the disease as it occurs in Canada.

Coté recognizes four main types of rape poisoning, his respiratory type being to some extent reminiscent of the syndrome of 'fog-fever' which occurs during autumn in several parts of Great Britain among cattle which have not necessarily had access to rape in any form.

He says that rape poisoning occurs more commonly in seasons of abnormal moisture and after early frost, and that rape grown on low-lying, poorly drained land is the most dangerous.

The *Respiratory Type* of poisoning is characterized by symptoms of acute pulmonary emphysema, i.e., sudden breakdown of the air cells of the lungs or 'broken-wind'; the affected animal remains apart from the others and does not feed, breathing becomes more distressed if the animal is forced to move. In acute cases, emphysema is sometimes found under the skin of the back. The temperature is seldom raised by more than one degree.

Post-mortem examination reveals emphysema and oedema of the lungs, which are brownish-grey in colour and distended. The digestive system contains a semi-solid mass of black ingesta and there is some inflammation of the intestines. Necrotic patches are occasionally found in the liver.

No effective treatment has yet been found for this type of disease.

The *Digestive Type* is seen three or four days after feeding on rape commences and may be due to the animals gorging on it. The affected animal is apart from the others, does not feed, and the abdomen appears to be tucked up. The temperature is normal. There is constipation and the sounds of rumen and bowel movements are absent. On rectal examination the rectum and colon are empty, except for small amounts of sticky black faeces which have a peculiar odour, there is gas in the colon but none in the rumen. The visible mucous membranes show the yellow coloration of jaundice.

Post-mortem examination shows the lungs to be normal, the rumen contents are black and there is no gas, the leaves of the omasum have a burned appearance and the mucous membrane peels easily from them. The contents of the small intestine are black and semi-solid and the mucous membrane is inflamed. The liver shows necrotic patches, the kidneys are inflamed, and the bladder contains dark-coloured urine.

Treatment consists of administering yeast, demulcents, stimulants, oily purges, and one pint of molasses. Epsom salts should not be given in this condition.

In the *Nervous Type* of the disease, affected animals become blind and maddened, they bore with their heads and batter everything with which they come in contact. No treatment is possible while an animal is in a fury, but those which have become blind and not violent have been successfully treated with hyposulphite of soda and one pint of molasses. Some animals remain blind permanently.

Post-mortem appearances are similar to those seen after death from the digestive type.

The *Urinary Type* is less deadly than any of the other three types. It is characterized by haemoglobinuria (red-water), the urine foaming as it falls to the ground. The visible mucous membranes are anaemic and jaundiced.

At post-mortem examination, the carcass is anaemic and appears to have been bled out. The liver shows necrotic areas and the kidneys are congested and show dark patches. The bladder contains gas and red-coloured urine.

Treatment. Preparations of iron are given with yeast and molasses.

Prevention of poisoning is of more value than attempts to cure the condition after it has occurred, and Coté recommends that hay should always be fed to cattle before folding them on rape and that they should have access to hay and straw and to an old meadow at all times. At first, they should only be folded on it for a short period, and this may be gradually increased until no restriction is necessary. Rape which shows purple discoloration is dangerous, and cattle should not be allowed to eat it.

Rape, in common with turnips and swedes, is capable of taking up large amounts of nitrate when grown on soil with a high nitrogen content, whether occurring naturally or the result of heavy applications of nitrogenous fertilizer. In this state it is as unsafe for sheep as for cattle and the author has no reason to suppose that once rape has become toxic it will ever become fit for feeding again.

Bruère (1956) records a mortality of 20 lambs, in a flock of 337, from nitrite poisoning, the result of feeding upon second growth rape.

Further information about nitrate and nitrite poisoning is to be found on page 50.

For further reading

CHARLOCK

Horses

S. P. KUNICYN, 1937, *Sovetsk. Vet.* (6) 68–9.
A. A. KOVALEV, 1937, *Sovetsk. Vet.* (10) 28–31.

Lambs

J. G. E. GALLIE and J. D. PATERSON, 1945, *Vet. Rec.* **57.** 198.

WHITE MUSTARD

Cattle

G. EATON, 1941, *Vet. Rec.* **53.** 146.

WILD RADISH

Sheep

TROUCHE, 1936, *Rev. vét., Toulouse,* **88.** 682–3.

KALE

Cattle

G. ROSENBERGER, 1939, *Dtsch. tierärtzl. Wschr.* **47.** 244–6.
G. M. DUNBAR and T. A. M. CHAMBERS, 1963, *Vet. Rec.* **75.** 566–7.

Goitrogens

RUTH ALLCROFT and F. J. SALT, 1961, *Advances in Thyroid Research.* Pergamon Press.
R. M. LOOSMORE, RUTH ALLCROFT *et al*, 1962, *Nature Lond.,* **193.** 595–6.

RAPE

Cattle

F. T. COTÉ, 1944, *Canad. J. comp. Med.* **8.** 38–41.

Lambs

N. BRUÈRE, 1956, *N.Z. Vet. J.* **4.** 128.

HYPERICACEAE

ST. JOHN'S WORT, Hypericum spp.

There are in the gardens, woodlands, hedgerows, grass verges and wilder parts of Britain some fifteen or more species of St. John's Wort. Several of these have been introduced as ornamental plants or as ground cover and have established themselves and become naturalized. Some of them remain quite local while others are widely distributed. The best known wild species is the almost ubiquitous Common St. John's Wort, (*Hypericum perforatum* L.) which can be found throughout England and Wales and in Southern Scotland. It is a perennial with a rhizomatous rootstock and an erect stem with two ridges, one on either side. The leaves are smooth and hairless without stalks or toothing and are arranged opposite each other on the stems. Held to the light they show numerous translucent dots. The flowers are seen from June to September. They have five bright yellow petals which are about twice as long as their five sepals.

Most, if not all, of the plants of the genus Hypericum contain a red coloured pigment, hypericin, which causes photo-sensitization of animals with little or no protective pigment in their skin, (see page 8). Species of the genus are distributed throughout temperate regions of both hemispheres and in mountainous areas of the tropics. When in the mountains of Kurdistan, the author considered that the large number of cases of photo-sensitization he encountered there among sheep were most likely to have been caused by St. John's Wort which they were seen to eat and which he was unable to distinguish from *H. perforatum*. St. John's Wort is widely established in New Zealand where it has become such a menace to farmers that large-scale campaigns have been undertaken for its eradication. Drying and storing, as in hay, do not lessen its photo-sensitizing effect.

For further reading

CONTROL

Agric. Gaz., N.S.W., 1936, **47.** 101–2, 313–4, 356–66, 608–10.

A. D. Imms, 1914, *Nature, Lond.* **153.** 785.

HYPERICIN

N. Pace and G. Mc'Kinney, 1941, *J. Amer. chem. Soc.* **63.** 2570–4.

CARYOPHYLLACEAE

The Pink family includes Soapwort (*Saponaria*), Corn Cockle (*Agrostemma*), Sandworts (*Arenaria*), Stitchworts (*Stellaria*) as well as such well-known garden flowers as pinks and carnations.

SOAPWORT, Crow-soap, or Hedge Pink (*Saponaria officinalis* L.)

Soapwort is a perennial with a fleshy creeping rootstock and several stout leafy stems, 1–2 feet high. The leaves are lanceolate and are marked with three or five parallel ribs. The flowers are pale pink and pleasantly scented. They are carried in dense heads at the top of the stems and open in August and September. It is found in most parts of Britain, in hedge banks and waste ground, chiefly near houses. Its name, soapwort, is derived from its use in times gone by, when the stems and leaves were gathered and either soaked or boiled in water, the resulting liquid being used for washing in the same manner as soap.

CORN COCKLE (*Agrostemma githago* L. syn. *Lychnis githago* (L.) Scop.)

Corn Cockle is an annual with long narrow leaves and long simple or slightly branched stems. The whole plant is covered with silky greyish or white hairs. The flowers are scentless and about 1½ inches in diameter. They are carried singly on long stalks, which arise from the leaf axils and are seen in July and August. The most peculiar feature of the flowers are the five long, narrow sepals, which are very much longer than the petals. There are five petals which are red or reddish purple. The seed capsules are large and open in five teeth, each capsule containing twenty to thirty rough-coated black seeds which have some resemblance to a curled-up caterpillar.

Formerly, it was a common weed of cornfields and, as the seeds ripen about the same time as the corn, it was threshed out with it and sown with the seed corn. With the advance of seed cleaning and dressing, it has almost disappeared from large areas of British arable land. The growing plant is avoided by livestock but the seeds, if mixed with corn or meal, are poisonous. In countries where threshing and milling are still primitive, corn cockle is an adulterant of wheat flour. The poisonous principle is not destroyed by baking, and bread containing it is of a greyish colour, with a bitter taste and unpleasant odour. Poisoning of livestock in Britain is likely only if the weed seeds from threshing and corn tailings are ground and mixed with other foodstuffs which may mask the taste and odour. Most animals refuse meals containing any quantity of these seeds. Dogs and young animals are most susceptible to their effects.

THYME-LEAVED SANDWORT (*Arenaria serpyllifolia* L.)

Thyme-leaved Sandwort is a small annual which is found in dry sandy places, more commonly in the southern counties than in the North. It is seldom above 6 inches in height, very slender, with many-branched stems, and the whole plant is covered with a fine down. The leaves are opposite on the stems and resemble those of thyme. The flowers are small, with five sepals which are longer than the five white petals.

CHICKWEED (*Stellaria media* (L.) Vill.)

Chickweed is a small, low-growing annual with very branched stems. It has a few hairs on the leaf stalks and a line of them along one side of the stems. The flowers are small and white with five petals which are shorter than the five sepals. They are seen from spring until late autumn. It is a common weed of cultivated places and is found throughout Britain.

Lambs have died through eating large quantities of chickweed, which has formed indigestible masses in their stomachs. Horses were reported by Cobbold to have been poisoned by it, or by another similar species of the same genus, during the Crimean War.

POISONING BY SAPONINS

All the members of the Pink Family described here contain poisonous colloidal glycosides known as saponins. They are so called because, although they do not dissolve in water, they suspend in it and impart to it a lathering or frothing capacity similar to soap. Should saponins enter the blood stream, they cause a breakdown or dissolution of the red blood corpuscles and of other important body cells (haemolysis). Dogs and young animals are more susceptible to the effects of saponins than other creatures. In Europe and in India, githagism, a chronic form of poisoning, has been recognized in human beings, dogs and horses. It is caused by ground corn cockle seeds in flour and milling offals. In this condition great lassitude, yawning, loss of weight and enteritis have been the chief symptoms, the patient wasting away and dying in a decline if the diet is continued.

Acute symptoms in all animals are gastro-enteritis with ulceration of the alimentary tract, frothy diarrhoea and general paralysis. Saponins are also believed to be one of the causes of the type of liver damage which gives rise to the formation of phylloerythrin and consequent photo-sensitization. Placidi (1954) states that poultry poisoned by corn cockle may show nervous symptoms similar to those seen in cases of Newcastle disease. At post-mortem examination, necrotic lesions may be found in the liver, spleen and lungs, as well as in the bowels, and the blood may be haemolysed.

Treatment of poisoning by saponins, from whatever source, is at first similar to the treatment of poisoning by irritants. Milk, eggs, sugar and a little salt are indicated, together with sedatives and anodynes if the pain is severe. Stimulants and careful nursing are required after the acute stages have passed. Laxatives should be limited to liquid paraffin until it can be reasonably supposed that the ulceration of the bowel walls has healed. It should go without saying that contaminated foodstuffs or access to the plants should be discontinued.

For further reading

CORN COCKLE POISONING IN POULTRY

R. FANGAUF and O. HAENSEL, 1934, *Landw. Geflügel Ztg.* Aug. 2.
G. F. HEUSER and A. E. SCHUMACHER, 1942, *Poult. Sci.* **21.** 86–93.
M. THERET, 1946, *Rec. Méd. vét.* **122.** 125–33.
L. PLACIDI, 1954, *Rec. Méd. vét.* **130.** 500–2.

CHENOPODIACEAE

Several of our most commonly grown fodder plants belong to the Goose-foot family: they include Sugar Beet (*Beta vulgaris* L. subsp. *esculenta* var. *altissima* Rössig.) and the Mangold, or Mangel Wurzel (*Beta vulgaris* L. subsp. *esculenta* (Salisb.) Gürke, syn. *B. rapa* Dum.). The weeds and wild plants of the family are not known to have caused poisoning in Britain, but Fat Hen (*Chenopodium album* L.) has caused trouble among lambs in New Zealand.

Scheuer-Karpin (1948) has recorded that human patients received hospital treatment in Dresden, Berlin, and Leipzig after having eaten Fat Hen (*C. album*) and Common Orache (*Atriplex patula* L.) two or three times daily for several weeks. They had picked these plants from rubble heaps and waste places and had used them as a vegetable when other green foods were unobtainable. All the patients recovered under treatment, but yellow pigmentation of the skin persisted for some time afterwards, particularly on the palms of the hands and soles of the feet. It was believed that saponins from the roots had caused the illness.

FODDER BEET, SUGAR BEET AND MANGELS

Fodder beet has become increasingly popular as a feed for pigs and cattle during recent years. Apart from the fact that pigs have to excrete large amounts of water when the roots are fed in excessive quantities, there have been few reports of ill-effects on these animals (Inglis, 1952). Injudicious feeding of fodder beet to cattle, however, may give rise to symptoms of poisoning. In Denmark, where fodder beet has been commonly fed to dairy cows for many years, roots with a dry-matter content of 17–18 per cent are regarded as most suitable for cows, while those with a higher dry-matter content, 22–24 per cent, are considered more likely to cause poisoning (Castle, 1953). Although certain individual cows may be able to stand quantities up to 90 lb of fodder beet per day without harm, when fed to herds much in excess of 30 lb per head per day, cases of poisoning may occur among them. As the dry-matter content of fodder beet is higher than that of most other feeding roots, it is customary to introduce them gradually into the diet, giving increasing amounts daily over a period of about a fortnight. When this precaution is neglected and they are suddenly added to the diet in comparatively large amounts, or when cattle steal and gorge upon them, cases of poisoning may be expected.

Sugar beet and mangels are too commonly grown as field crops to require description. Both have caused poisoning wherever they have been grown.

Horses seldom eat sufficient mangels to be poisoned or even adversely affected by them. They enjoy gnawing a whole mangel in their mangers during winter and early spring, and it is, without doubt, extremely good for them.

Sugar beet, however, in any form, is a highly dangerous food for horses. According to Mocsy (1936) hundreds of them have died in Europe from the effects of eating silage made from sugar beet tops. They suffer from a condition in which nervous symptoms predominate and usually take the form of spinal paralysis and, not infrequently, paralysis of the throat. The syndrome is reminiscent of botulism. Cattle which eat the same silage are not affected.

Although it cannot be classed as poisoning, brief mention of the choking of horses by sugar beet pulp is not out of place. In this animal, feeding with wet, molassed, or dried pulp, may result in impaction of the pulp in the gullet—in a mass which may extend from the stomach entrance to the throat. Dislodgement or removal of the mass is always difficult and in a large number of cases, impossible. Many hundreds of horses have died from the condition, and those which have recovered, have usually suffered for the remainder of their lives from strictures, due to damage of the gullet walls caused by the swelling of the pulp as it soaked up water and saliva.

Sugar beet pulp, unless fed with discretion, causes a fishy taint in the milk of dairy cows.

Mangels taken direct from the ground and fed to cattle or sheep, as all growers know, will cause illness and sometimes death. Consequently, they are ripened in a clamp and are not customarily fed to stock until after Christmas. The same applies to the tops and leaves of sugar beet, those from the earlier pulled crops particularly, being made into silage by many farmers.

The toxicity of root crops, in general, depends very much upon the nitrogen and the lime content of the soil in which they were grown and, after lifting, upon the effectiveness of the ripening process in the clamp or silo. Their harmful effects may be due to an excess of indigestible fibre, an excess of oxalic acid or soluble oxalates, an excess of nitrates and their conversion to nitrites or to any combination of them.

From highly nitrogenous soils, whether natural or acquired from fertilizer, the nitrate content of the crop is also high and the likelihood of this being converted to nitrite, either inside the rumen or outside the body, is that much greater. According to O'Moore (1955), about one-third of the nitrogen content of newly lifted mangels is in the form of pure protein, the remainder being in varying proportions of amides and nitrates. During normal ripening in the clamp or silo, a large part of the amides and nitrates combine to form amino acids and these may again link together to form protein and thus considerably reduce the risk of poisoning from this source.

Poisoning by nitrates, unless taken in very excessive quantities, is a relatively mild affair when compared with poisoning by nitrites and seldom invokes more than diarrhoea and diuresis, sometimes with blood-stained urine. Conversely, nitrite poisoning is much more serious and, depending upon the amount absorbed, may even cause sudden death. Nitrites are rapidly absorbed into the blood-stream where they exert their effects by combining with haemoglobin, the red colouring matter of the red blood corpuscles, to form methaemoglobin, a chocolate coloured, stable compound which will neither take up nor exchange oxygen and thus, unless the process can be rapidly reversed, badly affected animals may die very quickly from anoxaemia or oxygen starvation. Fortunately, methylene blue, an aniline dye, if administered early, is able to bring about a reversal but this may not always be available in time to prevent death in acute cases. For full effect a medium sized cow requires approximately 2 grams of the dye which should be dissolved in 50 ml water and injected intravenously. Other animals require proportionate doses of the same 4 per cent solution, according to their size.

Growing or newly-lifted mangels and beet tops also contain much larger amounts of oxalic acid and soluble oxalates than most other root crops. During ripening in the clamp or silo, oxalic acid and its soluble salts combine with other substances, chiefly calcium, to form insoluble compounds which are passed out of the body through the bowel without being absorbed into the blood-stream. In roots from lime-deficient soils, the ripening and the reduction of oxalates are often retarded and in many instances are only partial. Such roots, if fed in large quantities or over a long period, cause poisoning in those animals to which they are given. The condition is known as 'mangeld' in some parts of the country, and is as descriptive of the appearance of the sick animal as it is of the cause.

Oxalic acid and soluble oxalates are absorbed from the bowel into the blood-stream, where they combine with the calcium of the blood. This combination is requisite for removal by the kidneys, which excrete oxalates in the form of calcium oxalate. By denuding the blood of its calcium, the clotting power is considerably reduced, and, if the process goes far enough, may produce a condition similar to milk fever, particularly in heavily lactating cows and ewes. Calcium oxalate is not soluble in water, and crystals of it accumulate in the bladder and urethra, where it causes severe irritation and inflammation. Cows and ewes, with their short urethra and rapid emptying of the bladder are far less severely affected at this stage than bulls, bullocks, rams, and wethers. The male animals have a long, narrow urethra and micturition is slow when compared with the flushing flow of the female. Thus, the accumulation of the gritty sand-like crystals is greater and they may pass down and cause complete stoppage of the urethra at the S-shaped bend in the penis of the bull, and in the small worm-like extension of the urethra at the end of the penis of rams.

Symptoms in males are: slight elevation of the tail, frequent attempts at micturition, which may be non-productive or may result in the passage of a small quantity of urine which is often blood-stained. Colicky pains and tenderness over the loins are frequently shown, appetite and thirst are in abeyance, rumination ceases, and the rumen contains gas. Rectal examination reveals distension of the bladder, together with inflammatory swelling of the bladder neck and part of the urethra. Should there be blockage of the urethra at the S-shaped bend of the penis in bulls, or at the end of the penis of rams, the part of the urethra above the stoppage is distended with urine, and may be felt or seen below the anus. More acute cases in both males and females show 'paddling' with the hind limbs, staggering, and coma, a condition due to loss of calcium from the blood, and, in cause and symptoms, in almost every way similar to milk fever of cows.

Animals suffering from fodder-beet poisoning usually develop symptoms of sudden weakness, lie down and are unable to rise; a large proportion of a herd of cows or of younger animals may be found to be affected. The condition is somewhat reminiscent of milk fever, although the early symptoms of paddling gait and muscular stiffness usually associated with milk fever are not common features, and even though examination of blood from affected animals has shown that normal calcium, magnesium and acetone levels are maintained until near the point of death, in a high proportion of cases there is spectacular response to treatment by injection of calcium or magnesium, or of both. In cases which fail to respond or those which show any signs of cyanosis or blue discolouration of the visible mucous membranes, immediate treatment with methylene blue is indicated. A severe indigestion, in which rumination ceases and affected animals stand grinding their teeth and showing evidence of spasmodic abdominal pain, may also be seen; ruminal movement and defaecation are reduced or suspended and there is a marked fall in milk yield. Both forms of the disease may occur simultaneously in the same animal, and it is not unknown for an animal to recover from the milk-fever-like symptoms, only to die later from severe digestive disturbance.

First-aid treatment. Stop feeding with mangels or beet tops immediately, and give chalk to all animals which have been fed upon them. Affected animals should receive chalk and bicarbonate of soda as soon as possible after symptoms are noticed. These are the only medicaments likely to be found on the farm which are of any value in this condition, and the administration of proprietary drenches, or home-made medicines containing turpentine or spirits of sweet nitre is not only contra-indicated, but is positively dangerous to the life of the animal. The operation of urethrotomy may be necessary to relieve the bladder in cases of complete obstruction; it is not anatomically possible in bulls or rams to pass a catheter by the usual route. Where the worm-like appendage of the penis of rams is blocked, relief may often be obtained by rolling it gently between the well-lubricated forefinger and thumb, attempting to gradually break down the gritty mass. Injury or removal of this appendage may render a ram unable to fertilize ewes by normal service, although he may be used successfully for artificial insemination. In acute cases where symptoms are of the calcium deficiency type and animals are staggering or comatose, veterinary treatment with calcium or methylene blue injections is urgently required.

Prevention of oxalate poisoning is achieved very simply by adding common chalk to foodstuffs or by distributing lumps or blocks of it in mangers or pastures. Slaked lime and lime water have a similar effect, but they are not readily taken by animals. Many generations of farmers, by taking advantage of this knowledge, have been able to feed bullocks on large quantities of mangels, and sheep on sugar beet tops, as well as safely grazing cattle and sheep on pastures which contain a high percentage of such weeds as the sorrels which have a high oxalate content. Chalk is a form of calcium carbonate, and it combines in the stomach and bowels with oxalic acid and the soluble oxalates to form calcium oxalate, an insoluble salt, which is passed directly out of the bowel without being absorbed into the blood.

Pigs are seldom poisoned by oxalates from raw mangels or beet tops. This is because they are not fed on any large quantity of them rather than from insusceptibility. A different form of poisoning, however, which has caused great loss of pigs in many parts of the world, is due to the feeding of cooked roots. Turnips, swedes, red beet, sugar beet, and mangels, have all been involved. Each of these roots contains mineral salts in the form of nitrates, which are present in harmless amounts. Even if excessive quantities of the raw roots were eaten, the nitrates present would cause no more than a little extra urination. During cooking at temperatures below boiling point or when boiled quickly for a short period and then allowed to cool slowly in the water in which they were cooked, the nitrates in the roots are converted to nitrites, to which pigs have a far greater degree of susceptibility than the other farm animals.

Pigs fed upon boiled roots or upon the water in which they have been boiled may die very suddenly, within a matter of minutes after feeding, and without showing any previous symptoms. Those which survive a little longer may show signs of pain and great distress, vomiting, blue colour of the snout and mucous membranes, coma, convulsions, and death from asphyxia within an hour.

Post-mortem examinations reveal a pallid appearance of the skin around the snout and the coronets, blue colour of the visible mucous membranes (cyanosis), intense gastritis, venous congestion of the lungs, liver and kidneys and engorgement of the mesenteric veins. The blood in the organs and main vessels has the typical chocolate colour of methaemoglobin.

First-aid treatment is valueless in this condition. There may be some hope if a veterinary surgeon is available to administer methylene blue intravenously, but unless this is done very quickly after the commencement of symptoms it is useless.

Prevention of this type of poisoning is by not cooking roots at all, or by cooking them at boiling point or above for longer than two hours. The water in which they have been cooked should be strained off and discarded, and the roots allowed to cool as quickly as possible. It is believed by several authorities that the chemical change takes place during slow cooling.

For further reading

BEET

Pigs

GUEYNE, 1934, *Un. vét. Bordeaux* **13.** 5–8.
G. G. BENDINGER and M. J. JURKOW, 1935, *Tierärtztl. Rdsch.* **41.** 695–7.

Dogs

H. L. JONES, 1936, *Vet. Rec.* **48.** 1055–6.
J. M. BUCHANAN, 1936, *Vet. J.* **92.** 226–7.

Horses

J. MOCSY, 1936, *Allatorv. Közl.* **33.** 75.

Sheep

J. BRIERE, 1935, *Alfort Thesis*, 31.
J. MOTIEJUNAS, 1937, *Vet. ir. Zootech. Kovno.* **14.** 353–6.

Cattle

E. HUPKA, 1940, *Dtsch. tierärztl. Wschr.* **48.** 628–9.
F. CHAMBERS, 1944, *Vet. Rec.* **56.** 128.
Rep. Proc., B.V.A. Conf. on Metabolic Disorders, etc., Nov. 20–21, 1952.
M. E. CASTLE, 1953, *Agriculture*, **60.** 406–8.
A. N. WORDEN, *et al*, 1954, *Vet. Rec.* **66.** 133.

NITRATE

A SAVAGE, 1949, *Canad. J. comp. Med.* **13.** 9–10.

Cattle

GRAMATZSKI, 1950, *Dtsch. tierärztl. Wschr.* **57.** 347–9 and 400.

MANGELS

Pigs

B. FRANJO, 1937. *Jugosl. vet. Glasn.* **17.** 155–60.
W. D. ROBINSON, 1942, *N.Z. J. Agric.* **65.** 199–202.
I. G. MC'INTOSH, R. L. NIELSON and W. D. ROBINSON, 1943, *N.Z. J. Agric.* **66.** 341–3.

Pigs and Cows

J. MCLINTOCK, 1945, *Vet. Rec.* **57.** 384.

Cattle and Sheep

S. L. SNYDERS, 1945, *J. S. Afr. vet. med. Ass.* **16** 10–13.
J. W. H. HOLMES, 1946, *Vet. Rec.* **58.** 358.
L. B. O'MOORE, 1955, *Irish Vet. J.* **9.** 292–3.

SWEDES

Pigs

M. N. Nikolskii, 1940, *Sovetsk. Vet.* (4) 58–9.

FAT HEN

Lambs

F. J. Madden, 1943, *Yearb. Insp. Stk. N.S.W.* 25.

Human beings

R. Scheuer-Karpin, 1948, *Lancet* **254.** 574–5.

PHYTOLACCACEAE

POKEWEED, American Nightshade, Pigeonberry, (*Phytolacca americana* L.)

Pokeweed may stand from 4 feet to 6 feet high. It is a coarse glabrous perennial with a large fleshy root system. The stems are thick and the leaves, which are stalked, have a light green appearance with prominent veins. Flowers are small and are borne in a spike on the upper part of the plant. Berries form in late summer and autumn and pass from green to a reddish purple and then to almost black. When ripe the berries contain a red juice which somewhat resembles red ink. It has been introduced to this country from America and is grown in gardens and shrubberies from which it sometimes escapes and becomes naturalized.

All parts of the plant are poisonous particularly unripe berries, young shoots and roots. The toxicity is reduced somewhat in ripe fruits but even they can cause digestive disturbance if many are ingested. The toxic principles are a resin and a saponin.

There may be a delay of one to two hours between ingestion of the plant and the onset of symptoms, which may include severe purgation, vomiting where possible, drowsiness, narcosis and, in acute cases, coma and death.

This plant has caused a considerable amount of poisoning among children in U.S.A. as well as among animals.

First-aid for children is to induce them to vomit and keep them warm until medical advice can be obtained. Animals which can vomit should be treated similarly.

Barker & Farnes (1967) state that all parts of *P. americana* also contain a water soluble phytomitogen called pokeweed mitogen, which is capable of provoking blastogenesis in peripheral human blood lymphocytes. The phenomena exhibited by cells exposed to this phytomitogen being morphologically similar to that initiated by phytohaemagglutinin. *In vivo* human systemic exposure to pokeweed mitogen results in blastogenesis and mitosis of mononuclear cells in circulating blood as well as in the appearance of cells which, when stained by Romanowsky stain and viewed under the light microscope, are indistinguishable from plasma cells.

Another member of the same genus, *Phytolacca acinosa* Roxb., is reported to be more common as an alien in Britain than *P. americana* but the author has no information as to whether it is of comparable toxicity.

For further reading

B. E. Barker and P. Farnes, 1967, *Nature Lond.* **214.** 787–9.

MALVACEAE

MARSH MALLOW (*Malva* spp.)

Marsh Mallow has caused the death of sheep from staggers in Australia.

For further reading

H. McL. Gordon, 1936, *Aust. vet. J.* **12.** 29.

LINACEAE

COMMON FLAX, Linseed (*Linum usitatissimum* L.)

Common Flax is a tall, erect annual grown either for its seed or for the fibres contained within its stems. It has rich blue flowers with five petals and five sepals, and long narrow leaves which are alternate on the smooth stems. The seed capsules are globular in shape.

PURGING FLAX (*Linum catharticum* L.)

Purging Flax is an annual, much smaller than common flax, seldom standing more than 6 inches high. It has opposite leaves and tiny white flowers on long, slender pedicels. It is a weed of pastures and is found throughout Britain. Should it become too abundant in pastures, it may be eaten in sufficient quantities to cause diarrhoea.

Both common flax and purging flax contain a cyanogenetic glycoside, linamarin, and an enzyme, linamarase. When linamarin is activated by fermentation with linamarase, it produces prussic acid and glucose. The seeds of common flax, 'linseed', are used as animal foods, either as the whole seed or as a meal, and more commonly as a cake after the oil has been expressed. The content of linamarin in linseed is very variable and the enzyme, linamarase, which activates it, is not destroyed by soaking or by heating during the pressing of cakes. It is destroyed, however, by boiling for not less than ten minutes.

There is seldom sufficient prussic acid evolved from linseed, in any form, to affect adult animals, but sudden deaths occasionally occur among calves which receive proportionately larger quantities in the form of gruel.

Affected animals breathe rapidly, fall down, struggle violently as if in a convulsion, bleat pitifully and expire. Death may be so sudden that the preliminary symptoms pass unnoticed. Attempts to save the lives of calves affected in this way must be carried out rapidly. Artificial respiration, inhalations of ammonia and internal dosing with sugar or hyposulphite of soda (photographer's hypo) are about all that can be done in emergency. Prevention consists in boiling the linseed, meal, or cake for more than ten minutes and allowing it to cool slowly before feeding, or alternatively, to scald it and allow it to stand for six hours, stirring it several times in the interval to get rid of any acid which may have formed.

The effect of linamarin in small quantities differs from the acute symptoms described above. It is one of the known goitrogens and, if linseed cake or meal is fed over a long period to pregnant cows or ewes without supplementary iodine, thyroid dysfunction is very likely to result in the progeny. (See page 7.)

For further reading

M. A. M. Colin, 1937, *Alfort Thesis*, 48 pp.
A. D. Care, 1954, *N.Z. J. Sci. and Tech. Sec. A.* **36.** 321–7.

GERANIACEAE

COMMON STORKSBILL (*Erodium cicutarium* agg.)

Photo-sensitization has been observed among Friesian calves in Tasmania when grazed upon white clover (*Trifolium repens* L.) pastures which contained common storksbill.

For further reading

G. E. FORD, 1965, *Aust. Vet. J.* **41.** 56.

OXALIDACEAE

WOOD SORRELS (*Oxalis acetosella* L. and *O. corniculata* L.)

The wood sorrels contain oxalic acid. They are not likely to be eaten in sufficient quantities in Britain to do serious harm, but in Australia, where *O. corniculata* is more common, sheep have been poisoned by it. Both of these plants, if eaten by dairy cows, cause difficulty in churning the cream to butter.

For further reading

D. J. WALKER, 1939, *Yearbk. Insp. Stk. N.S.W.* 49–52.

CELASTRACEAE

The only member of the Spindle Tree family which grows wild in Britain is the spindle tree. Other members of the family, mostly imported from Europe, America and Japan are planted in ornamental shrubberies.

SPINDLE TREE or Skewer-wood (*Euonymus europaeus* L.) (Plate III)

The Spindle tree is a shrub which grows to a height of about 6 feet or more; it is found occasionally in woodlands and hedges, from Roxburgh southwards. The leaves, on short stalks, ovate-lanceolate in shape, are opposite on the short much-branched twigs. They are very minutely toothed at the edges and are about 1¼–1½ inches long at the time of flowering, but they continue to grow larger until the fruit is ripe, when they are about 3 or more inches long and 1½ inches broad. The flowers are seen in May or June. They have four sepals and the same number of petals and, when fully open, are about ⅓–½ inch in diameter. They are of a pale yellowish-green or greenish-white colour and are carried in cymes of three or five on short stalks which arise from the leaf axils.

The fruit, when ripe, is of a striking bright red colour. It has four lobes, each making a cell for a single seed, and when it opens shows the bright orange-yellow aril which covers each seed. Most Continental writers, French and German, liken the fruit to priests' hats, but as very few priests in Britain wear hats of the biretta type, this name conveys little to the average British reader.

The wood is hard and was sought after by gypsies and others for the manufacture of spindles, knitting needles, skewers and pegs, and for burning to make charcoal drawing sticks. Cornevin says that the bark, the leaves and the fruits are poisonous. At the end of the summer when the fruits are formed, the leaves become less poisonous. Several cases are known of poisoning of sheep and goats which have eaten the twigs and leaves.

The pretty colouring of the fruits in autumn makes them particularly attractive to children.

Horses will eat spindle tree in spite of its unpleasant odour and as a result suffer from violent purgation. Poisoning of horses by it is described by Gessner (1943).

There appears to be much doubt as to the active principle involved. Euonymine, a bitter, crystalline substance, soluble in alcohol and ether, described as toxic by Cornevin, has not been confirmed by other workers. It is, however, certain that the ingestion of sufficient spindle tree will cause violent and persistent purgation in animals that eat it.

Treatment is similar to that for any acute purgation. Warmth, water slightly warmed, astringents, and sedatives if necessary; stimulants may be given if the patient is weakened.

For further reading

O. Gessner, 1943, *Berl. Münch. tierärztl. Wschr.* (7–8) 47–8.

BUXACEAE

BOX (*Buxus sempervirens* L.)

Box is a well-known evergreen shrub which is found wild on chalky and limestone soils in the southern half of England. It is cultivated and naturalized as an ornamental shrub in most other parts of the country. It is commonly seen between three to fifteen feet high, but under favourable conditions may attain thirty feet, with a stem up to three feet in diameter. The small box hedges which are grown as an ornamental edging around flower-beds, etc., are a dwarf variety.

Box wood has a very fine grain and is extremely hard. It is used in the manufacture of drawing instruments and special tools, mallet-heads for lead working, etc.

The leaves, which are opposite on the branches, are elliptical with a notch at the apex and about half to one inch long. The white flowers, which appear in April or May, are unisexual, but flowers of both sexes are together in small clusters in the leaf axils. The fruit is a hard ovoid capsule terminating with three short beaks and contains six shining black seeds.

All parts of the plant are poisonous and are believed to contain an alkaloid, buxine (Faure 1830). It was later said by Flückiger to be identical with pelosine and bebeerine, and was regarded as a separate entity by Scholtz. Further investigation is required before it can be definitely regarded as the poisonous principle, as the shrub contains a resin and an essential oil in addition. Whether the toxic principle of box is any one of these, or a combination of them all, it still remains an acutely irritant poison.

The bark and underlying wood of young branches have been scraped and given in food to horses as a tonic. The author has, on one occasion only, seen poisoning in a cart-horse by this practice. There was no possibility of ascertaining how much had been ingested, as the scraped wood and bark had been mixed in a coffer already half full of mixed chaff and oats, from which the horse had been fed. When seen, the animal was in intense pain, sweating was profuse and there was some salivation; the abdominal muscles were tensed and were tender on palpation. Although there was obvious abdominal pain, the horse refused to lie down, or if he did so, immediately rose again. The pain abated slightly after four hours, when blood-stained diarrhoea commenced. This lasted for a day, and was followed by laminitis. The animal recovered after a long convalescence. A young pony which ate the growing plant while straying into a garden was not so fortunate. He died from super-purgation and acute lung congestion about sixteen hours later. Again, it was noted that he would not attempt to lie down, and actually died on his legs.

Post-mortem examination revealed acute gastritis and enteritis with bloody effusion into the bowel; the lungs were acutely congested and oedematous, and death was due to asphyxia.

There is a popular belief that box leaves are good for aquarium fish. The author has on several occasions seen every fish killed by putting sprigs of box into the water of tropical tanks.

Pigs are also susceptible to poisoning by box leaves; they show symptoms of vomiting and abdominal pain, followed by bloody diarrhoea and acute lung congestion. They may die from the latter before diarrhoea commences.

First-aid treatment should be as for other irritant poisons—eggs, skimmed milk, sugar, starch, gruel, etc. (see page 15).

RHAMNACEAE

The Buckthorn family is represented in Britain by the Common or Purging Buckthorn (*Rhamnus cathartica*) on chalky soils and the Alder Buckthorn (*Frangula alnus* Mill.) on peaty and leafy soils. They are very branched shrubs with alternate, undivided leaves and small green flowers. They are not common in England and are almost unknown in Scotland.

COMMON BUCKTHORN (*R. cathartica* L.)

The common Buckthorn is a much-branched shrub standing 5–10 feet in height. The branchlets, which are opposite, terminate in a sharp strong thorn. The leaves are ovate and pointed, with regularly serrated edges and are carried on stalks. They are about 1½–2 inches long, and though small at the time of flowering, grow larger as the fruits are formed.

The flowers are dioecious, very small (less than ¼ inch in diameter) and of a yellowish-green colour. They are found in clusters on short pedicels in the leaf axils. The male flowers have four petals and four stamens which are longer than the petals. The female flowers, which are smaller than the males, have a style with four lobes. The black fruit is about the size of a black currant and contains four stones.

ALDER BUCKTHORN, Black Alder (*Frangula alnus* Mill. syn. *Rhamnus frangula* L.) (Plate I)

The Alder Buckthorn is a more erect shrub than the Common Buckthorn. It has alternate branches and no thorns, the leaves are broader and not toothed and when young have minute hairs on the under-side. The flowers are bisexual, and two or three are found together in each leaf axil. They are yellowish-green in colour with five sepals, five petals, and five stamens and

Greater Celandine (*Chelidonium majus* L.)

Alder Buckthorn (*Frangula alnus* Mill.)

PLATE I

St. John's Wort (*Hypericum perforatum* L.)

Stinking Hellebore (*Helleborus foetidus* L.

Water Dropwort (*Oenanthe crocata* L.)

Spindle Tree (*Euonymus europaeus* L.) Fruits and Leaves

PLATE III

Black Nightshade (*Solanum nigrum* L.)

Deadly Nightshade (*Atropa belladonna* L.)

Dog's Mercury (*Mercurialis perennis* L.)

Henbane (*Hyoscyamus niger* L.) in fruit

PLATE V

Top: Mezereon (*Daphne mezereum* L.)
Bottom: Spurge Laurel (*Daphne laureola* L.)
PLATE VI

Yew Twig (*Taxus baccata* L.

Black Bryony (*Tamus communis* L.)

PLATE VII

Meadow Saffron (*Colchicum autumnale* L.)

Foxglove (*Digitalis purpurea* L.)

are seen from May to July. The fruit is globular, about the size of a pea, and is darkish purple in colour. The alder buckthorn is more widely distributed in England than the common buckthorn and is found on peaty or leafy soils. It is rarely found in Scotland.

The buckthorns have been used as laxatives in medicine from time immemorial. A syrup prepared from the berries of the common buckthorn has been a common laxative for dogs, and an extract from the dried and stored bark of the alder buckthorn has been used as a purgative for patients with liver trouble. Cascara sagrada, a common household laxative, is prepared from the bark of a member of the same family (*Rhamnus purshiana* DC), imported from America. The leaves have been administered to reduce the secretion of milk in human beings and animals.

The fruits of both species are dangerous to children. If eaten, they cause super-purgation and collapse. The leaves and bark of the alder buckthorn are gastro-intestinal irritants when fresh, but after drying and storage for a year or more, they have an action similar to aloes. The active principles are glycosides, which break down to yield emodin. The poisoning of a cow with alder buckthorn is described by Södermark (1942).

Treatment of poisoning by buckthorn is similar to that used for any other irritant and for super-purgation.

For further reading

N. SÖDERMARK, 1942, *Svensk Vet. Tidskr.* abst. in *Skand. Vet. Tidskr.* **32.** 458.

LEGUMINOSAE

The legume or peaflower family includes many of the most widely grown fodder plants, such as the clovers, peas and beans, as well as a few poisonous species like laburnum and the lupins.

LUPINS (*Lupinus* spp.)

The Lupins are not native British plants and are seldom found wild except as escapes from cultivation. They are commonly grown in gardens for their flowers. The yellow lupin (*Lupinus luteus* L.) and the blue lupin (*L. angustifolius* L.) are extensively grown as green manure and fodder crops throughout the world. In Britain, blue lupins have been grown in the eastern and southern counties, where they are folded with sheep or ploughed in.

The blue lupin is an annual herb which grows to about 3 feet in height. The leaves are digitate on long stalks and have five to nine leaflets which are covered with soft hairs. The flowers are blue and are carried on short pedicels in a raceme at the top of the stems, the lower ones opening earlier than those above them. The fruit is a pod which is covered with soft hairs and contains up to six seeds.

The yellow lupin is reputed in Europe to be the more dangerous, but the blue lupin has been responsible for many losses among the world's sheep. There is some controversy as to why lupins in one season are much more toxic than in another, and many theories have been propounded. The alkaloids responsible for lupin poisoning or 'lupinosis', are, in the yellow lupin, lupinine and *l*-sparteine or lupinidine; and in the blue lupin, *l*- and *dl*-lupanine and hydroxylupanine. The alkaloids are found in greater concentration in the seeds than elsewhere in the plant, and cases of lupinosis are mostly recorded of sheep which have been folded upon crops after pods were well formed. Drying and storage have no effect upon the poisons, and hay made from a crop which has passed the safe grazing stages is just as dangerous to animals as the fresh plants would have been. Research by plant breeding stations in many parts of the world has been directed towards the production of non-poisonous varieties, and among others, the Sweet Blue lupin is comparatively free from alkaloids.

The symptoms of acute lupinosis are loss of appetite, reluctance to move, some difficulty in breathing, blood-stained urine, trembling, staggering, and death from asphyxia. Jaundice is characteristic of both the acute and chronic forms, and Brash (1943) describes swelling of the head and photo-sensitization among his cases in New Zealand. The alkaloids are rapidly excreted from the body by the kidneys and are not cumulative, but the damage done to the liver may make recovery comparatively slow. In Australian sheep, Gardiner (1966) believes that those with a high copper content in the liver are more susceptible to lupinosis than others.

Post-mortem examination reveals jaundicing throughout the carcass, hepatitis and fatty degeneration of the liver, catarrhal inflammation and distension of the gall bladder and enlargement of the spleen. The stomachs show inflammation and there may be an effusion of blood into the bowels, bladder and peritoneum.

First-aid treatment consists of removing all sheep from any possible access to lupins or lupin hay. Acids neutralize the poisons, and all sheep which show dullness or are not feeding should be drenched with vinegar and water. This should be accompanied, or followed later, by an easily assimilated carbohydrate such as sugar or molasses to aid in the restoration of liver functions. Any which show swelling of the head should be housed and shaded from strong light.

Although sheep are the animals most commonly affected by lupins, the other domesticated animals are susceptible to their effects. Pigs, accidentally poisoned by lupin seeds in Poland, suffered from gastritis and jaundice. Two died out of eighty-seven affected.

LABURNUM (*Laburnum anagyroides* Medic. syn. *Cytisus laburnum* L.)

The Laburnum is a well-known ornamental tree, grown for its golden-yellow flowers which hang like bunches of grapes in spring and early summer. The wood was much valued in the past for the manufacture of gun-stocks and small turned articles because of the high polish that could be imparted to it. The leaves, which are on long stalks, are trifoliate. The leaflets are light green in colour and have a minutely fine down on the underside.

The fruit is a pod about 2–2½ inches long. It contains up to eight kidney-shaped seeds which become dark brown to black when dry.

After the yew tree, the laburnum is the most poisonous tree grown in Britain; all parts of it are toxic, the wood, bark and roots being consistently so throughout the year, but the leaves lose some of their poison as the fruits ripen and the seeds mature; it concentrates in the pods and seeds.

The poisonous principle is the alkaloid, cytisine; a most dangerous substance, and it is similar in its actions on the body to nicotine; it is excreted by the kidneys and may be found in the urine. Numerous cases are recorded of laburnum poisoning of human beings who have eaten the flowers or seeds, or who have carried twigs or bunches of flowers in their mouths. The symptoms are dilation of the pupils, stomach pains, vomiting, giddiness, muscular weakness, coldness of the limbs, inco-ordination, convulsions and death from asphyxia.

In any case where laburnum poisoning is suspected in children or adults, medical aid should be sought immediately, and preparations made for enemata and stomach pumping to be carried out. In the meantime an emetic may be given and the patient kept quiet and warm. Because the poison affects the respiratory centres, artificial respiration should be started at the first sign of difficulty in breathing and should be continued until the medical adviser gives other directions.

Severe illness and death occur in animals, most commonly after eating the seeds or pods. They seldom eat the leaves or flowers. Horses are more susceptible to its effects than ruminants and are more commonly affected by it, while poultry and pigeons do not appear to pick up the seeds. The author has attended three horses poisoned by laburnum: a child's pony, which had eaten a feed of oats spilled by its youthful owner onto the ground under a laburnum tree, and gathered up again together with a considerable amount of fallen laburnum pods and seeds; and two carthorses, which had been temporarily tied to a laburnum tree for about an hour and had eaten leaves and hanging pods. In each case symptoms occurred between four and five hours after ingestion. They all showed incoordination of the limbs, sweating, tremors and muscular contractions, and only slight colic. All of them became comatose and died within four hours of the commencement of symptoms. Post-mortem examination revealed large quantitites of seeds and pods in the stomach; otherwise there was little pathological change.

Although cattle and goats are more resistant to the effects of laburnum than horses, two occurrences of poisoning in cattle while the tree was leafless are recorded by Connolly (1949), in one of which twelve cattle were involved and one died and, in the other, four bullocks were affected and recovered. Auchterlonie (1948) records that a heifer which ate the leaves gave bitter-tasting milk with yellow clots and returned to normal after six weeks. She did not suffer from diarrhoea. He also records that a pig fed on laburnum leaves and grass recovered after suffering from acute dysentery and blanching of the mucous membranes.

First-aid treatment of animals must depend upon the symptoms, and consists chiefly in keeping the patient warm and quiet until veterinary aid is obtained. There is no specific antidote to cytisine.

COMMON BROOM (*Sarothamnus scoparius* (L.) Koch. syn. *Cytisus scoparius* (L.) Link and Spanish Broom (*Spartium junceum* L.).

Common Broom is to be found in dry, waste places and in gardens throughout Britain. Spanish Broom is also frequently planted. Their brilliant yellow flowers and erect, green, wiry branches are well known.

A great deal of superstition and erroneous belief in the magical and poisonous qualities of broom still persists in many parts of the country; much of it dating back to the days when witches used broomsticks in their rituals and prescribed broom-tops as the panacea for all female ailments, and dropsy.

Broom contains very small quantities of the poisonous alkaloids cytisine and sparteine and a glycoside, scoparin. They are present in such small amounts that the likelihood of an animal eating sufficient of the plant to cause poisoning is very remote. Lander computed that 25 lb of the plant would be required to poison a horse.

POISONING BY OTHER SPECIES OF THE PEAFLOWER FAMILY

Several members of the Peaflower family, grown chiefly as fodder, have been the cause of poisoning in many parts of the world. Only those commonly seen on British farms are mentioned here. It must always be remembered that under British conditions of farming and feeding, one species of plant seldom forms the sole diet of our livestock for lengthy periods and, because of this, poisoning from fodder crops is less likely than in many places overseas.

Poisoning of cattle by White Clover (*Trifolium repens* L.) has been recorded on many occasions in New Zealand. A few strains were found which contained a cyanogenetic glycoside, lotaustralin, which is activated by the enzyme linamarase to produce hydrocyanic (prussic) acid. These toxic strains have also been responsible for the production of goitrogens in ewes, with consequent abortion and birth of goitrous lambs. Research into the genetics of white clover has resulted in the production of glycoside-free strains.

In Britain, pasturing cattle upon white clover which had seeded, the seeds having sprouted again in the flower heads, has been considered to be the cause of a disease similar to acute laminitis with separation of the hooves, followed by sloughing below the pastern and exostosis of metacarpal and metatarsal bones.

Alsike Clover (*Trifolium hybridum* L.), Common Vetch (*Vicia sativa* L.), Lucerne (*Medicago sativa* L.) and Hairy Medick (*Medicago polymorpha* L. emend. Shinners) have caused photo-sensitization or 'trifoliosis' with its attendant liver disturbance in horses, cattle and sheep wherever they have been grown. In Canada, 'Big liver disease' (chronic hypertrophic cirrhosis) of horses, with symptoms of jaundice, dark coloured urine and wasting, was considered to be caused by alsike clover by Schofield (1933) who succeeded in reproducing the condition in twelve horses by feeding them on alsike. In Europe and Asia, however, almost identical syndromes have been observed when horses have been fed for a period on any one of the above. In America, a cyanogenetic glycoside has been found in the seeds of common vetch.

LATHYRISM

The toxicity of the seeds of most species of *Lathyrus*, particularly for horses has long been recognised. During the latter half of the nineteenth century, seeds of the Indian or mutter pea (*Lathyrus sativus* L.) were imported into Britain as stock-feed. Cattle appeared to be unaffected by them, even when given in quantity, but when fed to horses they suffered from a spastic paralytic condition which affected both the larynx and the hind quarters. During exercise the horse became suddenly attacked with acute dyspnoea, often to a state of near suffocation, and fell to the ground apparently suffering from paralysis of the hind quarters. After a comparatively short rest the horse usually recovered sufficiently to be able to rise again and return slowly to the stable, although, occasionally, the paroxysms were so severe that they proved fatal.

A very similar condition, due to the same cause and also known as lathyrism, affects human beings, particularly young people, in India and in Spain when, during times of famine or acute financial stress, they are forced to eat this pea. Both man and horse suffer from spastic paraplegia, which is inclined to be progressive, and there is not uncommonly a delay of anything from four days to seven weeks between the cessation of feeding upon lathyrus seeds and the onset of symptoms.

In Spain, it is always believed that horses are less susceptible to lathyrism than mules, in which the mortality rate is often as high as 25 per cent.

Experimentally, the disease has been caused by feeding seeds of Sweet Pea (*Lathyrus odoratus* L.), Hairy Vetchling (*L. hirsutus* L.) and Everlasting Pea (*L. sylvestris* L.) to horses and to rats but the latter develop a different syndrome from that described.

Similar outbreaks from feeding growing, but in-pod vetches and tares, are not unknown in Spain and North Italy and Greatorex (1966) reports an outbreak among four riding horses in England. Before they first fell while out at exercise, these horses had been fed for ten to twelve days upon hay which was composed of 85 to 90 per cent of Grass Vetchling (*L. nissolia* L.) which was in the pod stage and well seeded. All recovered within a few days after a change of diet and none of them were reported to have suffered from the acute laryngeal stridor which commonly precedes the fall.

GROUNDNUT, Earthnut, Peanut, Monkeynut. (*Arachis hypogaea* L.)

Except perhaps as a greenhouse novelty, to demonstrate its habit of burying its young seed pods in the ground to mature and ripen, after its pretty blue flowers have been fertilized in the air, groundnut is not grown in Britain. Large quantities of the nuts, and cake and meal which are the residues after expression or extraction of the oil, are, however, imported annually from tropical countries for stock-feed.

Groundnut has always been considered as one of the safest of all feeds for livestock and any suspicion of toxicity has, until recent years, been generally blamed on cyanogenetic glycosides which a few strains were believed to contain. After an outbreak of disease among young turkey poults and further outbreaks among ducklings and pheasant chicks, it appeared that the only common factor was groundnut meal in the ration. This, after considerable research, was found to contain aflatoxin, a complex of mycotoxins which is produced by a mould (*Aspergillus flavus*) and which was proved to be the causal factor (see page 18). Groundnut is not the sole medium for the growth of the mould, *A. flavus*; it can grow and produce its toxins on any cereal or oilseed which is stored under sufficiently moist conditions. Slow drying of nuts with damaged shells, insufficient cover from rain, wetting during transport in the country of origin and the usual hazards attendant upon sea travel in poorly ventilated holds from the tropics to Europe, all favour mould growth.

There seems to be little reason for hope that, once mould growth has commenced, there is any liklihood of a simple method being devised which will remove aflatoxin and render the nuts suitable for animal feeding again, without causing a very considerable loss of nutritive value.

Although the losses occasioned by the outbreaks mentioned were enormous, the discovery of the cause and the great awareness of importers and feed compounders of its dangers have greatly reduced any risk of further recurrence. There are no recorded instances of human poisoning by aflatoxin in groundnuts nor is its likelihood very great in Britain. Great care is taken at the ports to ensure that infected nuts are not imported for human consumption and, even if they were, the amount eaten at any one time would not be a serious menace to health. It is known that at least one substance of the complex which comprises aflatoxin is capable of being excreted in the milk of lactating animals but, even if it were known whether humans are susceptible to its effects, the amount of groundnut cake or meal normally included in dairy cow rations is so small that poisoning from this source could be discounted.

Groundnut oil is a widely used commodity and the refining process, to which it is subjected after pressing or extraction, ensures its freedom from aflatoxin, so no fears need be entertained about the wholesomeness of foods, in the preparation of which it has been used.

For further reading

LUPIN

A. G. Brash, 1943, *N.Z. J. Agric.* **67.** 83–4.
M. H. Gardiner, 1966, *J. Comp. Path.* **76.** 107–20.

LABURNUM

L. Auchterlonie, 1948, *Vet. Rec.* **60.** 633.
F. Connolly, 1949, *Irish Vet. J.* **3.** 266–8.

ALSIKE

F. W. Schofield, 1933, *Circ. Ont. vet. Coll.* **52.** 4.

LUCERNE AND TREFOIL

K. V. Byrne, 1937, *Aust. vet. J.* **13.** 74–5
1937, *Agric. Gaz. N.S.W.* **48.** 214.
P. L. Chelle, 1940, *Rec. Méd. vét.* **116.** 5–16.
C. C. Morrill, 1943, *N. Amer. Vet.* **24.** 731–2.
M. G. Fincher and H. K. Fuller, 1942, *Cornell Vet.* **32.** 95–8.

PAPILIONACEAE

M. G. Fincher and H. K. Fuller, 1942 *Cornell Vet.*, **32** 95–8.

LATHYRISM

E. Ortiz de Landazari and A. Galdo Seco, 1949, *Rev. Clin. Española.* **32.** 29–32.
J. C. Greatorex, 1966, *Vet. Rec.* **78.** 725–7.
C. I. Levene, 1966, *Proc. Roy. Soc. Med.* **59.** 757–8.

GROUNDNUTS (AFLATOXIN)

Cattle

R. M. Loosmore and L. M. Markson, 1961, *Vet. Rec.* **73.** 813–4.
R. Allcroft and G. Lewis, 1963, *Vet. Rec.* **75.** 487–94.

Milk

R. Allcroft, H. Rogers, G. Lewis, J. Nabney and P. E. Best, 1966, *Nature* **209.** 154–5.

Pigs

R. M. Loosmore and J. D. J. Harding, 1961, *Vet. Rec.* **73.** 1362–4.
J. D. J. Harding, J. T. Done, G. Lewis and R. Allcroft, 1963, *Res. Vet. Sci.* **4.** 217–29.

ROSACEAE

The Rose family comprises many of the most commonly grown fruit trees: apple, pear, plum, cherry, peach, apricot and almond. The kernels of all these and the leaves of the Cherry Laurel (*Prunus laurocerasus* L.) contain a cyanogenetic glycoside, amygdalin, which, when acted upon by the enzyme, emulsin, gives off hydrocyanic acid. In the British Isles, reports of poisoning by members of this family have been rare, and the author can find no reference later than 1941, when Robb and Campbell, and Wilson and Gordon, reported the poisoning of sheep from eating cherry laurel. In New Zealand, calves have died from eating cherry laurel (Gill and Macgregor 1928). Occasionally the death of children from eating apricot or peach kernels is reported from abroad, and York (1942) reports cherry stones as the source of prussic acid which caused deaths in a flock of American chickens.

CHERRY LAUREL (*Prunus laurocerasus* L.)

The Cherry Laurel is an evergreen shrub commonly seen in gardens and shrubberies. The leaves are 3–6 inches long, hard, and shining. The sweetly scented, white flowers are in a slender raceme seldom longer than the leaves. The fruits, from which the name is derived, somewhat resemble black cherries. Animals eat little of it from choice, and, it would appear that when grown under British conditions its poisonous qualities are much lower than in other European countries. It should, however, be borne in mind as one of the possible causes of sudden death.

For further reading

CHERRY LAUREL

W. Robb and D. Campbell, 1941, *Vet. Rec.* **53**. 93–5.
D. R. Wilson and W. S. Gordon, 1941, *Vet. Rec.* **53**. 95–7.

CRASSULACEAE

SEDUM spp.

Both Wall-pepper, Gold-dust, or Common Stonecrop (*Sedum acre* L.) and White Stonecrop (*S. album* L.) are reputed to be poisonous, but as they usually grow in such inaccessible places as old walls and rocks, they are very unlikely to cause poisoning.

THYMELEACEAE

The only indigenous species of the Daphne family are the Mezereon (*Daphne mezereum* L.) and the Spurge Laurel (*Daphne laureola* L.). Other exotic genera, such as the tender Australasian pimeleas, are sometimes cultivated.

MEZEREON, Dwarf Bay Tree, Spurge Olive (*Daphne mezereum* L.) (Plate VI)

The Mezereon is an erect, glabrous shrub which stands 1–3 feet in height. It is probably only found wild in woodlands in the southern counties of England, but because of the great beauty and sweet fragrance of its flowers it is a popular favourite and is cultivated in gardens and shrubberies throughout the country. The flowers are pink to purple in colour and appear in clusters on the previous year's shoots, very early in spring before the leaves are out. The leaves are lanceolate, about 2–3 inches long, and appear in tufts at the end of the branches as the flowers die down. The fruit is a berry, having some resemblance to a red currant in size and colour.

Because of the acrid irritant juice which pervades all parts of the plant, particularly the bark and berries, animals do not usually eat them. Cases of human poisoning, chiefly among women and children who have eaten them in mistake for red currants, are not uncommon in the literature.

Nicholson, in *Lander's Veterinary Toxicology* states that the mezereon contains an acrid substance, mezerinic acid, which is an intensely irritant poison not destroyed by drying and storage. Little is known of its chemical properties, and isolation of it by analysis is neither easy nor definite.

Children who have eaten the berries suffer from a burning sensation in the mouth and stomach, with swelling of the tongue and lips, vomiting, rapid weak pulse, and great prostration; collapse and death may follow.

During the last war, the author investigated the sudden death of six out of a litter of seven young pigs, about ten weeks old. Post-mortem examination showed intense gastritis with white patches in the stomach which had a burned appearance; similar patches were found in the mouth and pharynx and on the tongue. All had vomited before death and their stomachs were empty of ingesta. An evacuee child, unused to the country, had picked mezereon berries from a bush in the garden thinking that they were red currants, and after tasting one and finding that it burned his mouth and tongue had ejected it again quickly without swallowing it. He threw the remainder of the berries into a trough, from which the pigs were feeding at the time The surviving pig was the 'rickling' or 'runt' of the litter, which had apparently been kept away from the trough by the others while the berries were eaten. Examination of the inside of the child's mouth showed similar white patches, from which the surface sloughed later, leaving raw ulcers which received medical treatment. Careful examination of the mezereon bush revealed the places from which nineteen berries had been taken, an average of three per pig.

First-aid treatment. Give an emetic immediately, salt and water is perhaps best for children, treat with demulcents: egg sugar, milk (see pages 13 and 15).

SPURGE LAUREL, Wood Laurel (*Daphne laureola* L.) (Plate VI)

Spurge Laurel is more common in English woodlands than the mezereon but is rarely, if ever, found wild in Scotland. It is an erect glabrous shrub, larger than the mezereon, attaining a height up to about 4 feet. It has a thick stem, marked with the scars of fallen leaves and is sparingly branched. The leaves are evergreen, about 4 inches long and 1½ inches wide, and are clustered towards the ends of the branches. The flowers are in short racemes in the leaf axils; they are green in colour and are sweet-scented for a period (Hutchinson). They are smaller than those of mezereon and are seen later in spring. The fruit is an egg-shaped, bluish-black berry.

The spurge laurel, like its cousin the mezereon, is extremely poisonous in all its parts, especially the bark and berries. Children are attracted by the berries and death may result from eating them.

Animals do not usually eat the leaves because of their acrid taste, due to the same active principle as that of the mezereon. *Lander's Veterinary Toxicology* describes the case of horses poisoned by dried spurge laurel. They showed intense colic with primary constipation followed later by super-purgation, the evacuations containing blood, mucus, and intestinal epithelium. A horse, which ate the growing shrub, showed lack of appetite the same night; next day there was abdominal pain, staggering gait, anxious countenance and laboured breathing, pulse 80, temperature 103·2°F, bowels normal. On the following day there was excessive purgation, pulse 120, temperature 104·2°F, and death occurred at midday.

Post-mortem examination revealed inflammation of the stomach and intestines, fluid ingesta, excessive thickening of the colon with blood-stained contents and a peculiar odour.

First-aid treatment is similar to that described for mezereon and other irritant poisons.

LORANTHACEAE

MISTLETOE (*Viscum album* L.)

Mistletoe is a much branched somewhat woody evergreen which is parasitic on the branches of many deciduous trees, often on apple, pear and oak and sometimes on poplar. The fruit is a globose white translucent berry which is ripe at Christmas and contains a sticky viscous juice and a single seed.

Mistletoe berries have long been known to be poisonous for children and animals should they eat many of them. The toxic principle, according to Samuelson (1961–62), is a polypeptide, viscotoxin A.

Greatorex (1966) reports that a six months old griffon showed posterior incoordination fifteen hours after eating a spray of well berried mistletoe. This progressed to paralysis with opisthotonic muscular contractions and rapid respirations and pulse. Temperature remained normal until close to death which occurred 50 hours after eating the plant. Post-mortem examination showed slight hyperaemia of stomach, intestines, liver and brain, and some oedema of perirenal region, lymph nodes, lungs and meninges. The kidneys appeared pale macroscopically and the liver showed some fatty changes microscopically.

For further reading

M. H. CHAPRON, 1936, *Rev. Path. Comp.* **36.** 400–1.
G. SAMUELSON, 1961, *Svensk. farm. Tidsk.* **65.** 209, 481.
1962, ibid, **66.** 201, 237.
J. C. GREATOREX, 1966, *Vet. Rec.* **78.** 726.

ARALIACEAE

IVY (*Hedera helix* L.)

Ivy is the only plant in the Aralia family which is a native of Britain. It is a well-known woody evergreen which is found climbing on trees, rocks and buildings throughout the country. It is recognized by its thick shiny leaves, which usually have three or five lobes, the central one being the longest. The flowers are seen in late autumn, they are yellowish-green and occur in short racemes or panicles of nearly globular umbels, carried on flowering branches which arise from the main stems. The fruits are smooth black globular berries. An infusion of the leaves is still used in country districts as a fomentation for bruises and for the removal of shiny patches on clothes.

From the earliest times the berries of ivy have been considered to be poisonous. Children have been the chief victims, and a case has been reported of human poisoning by the leaves.

It is not considered to be harmful to livestock in small quantities, and a young branch is often offered as a tonic to sickly cattle, sheep and goats.

The author saw two Jersey cows ill as the result of eating large quantities of the leaves and apparently the berries. Long-neglected ivy had been stripped from the side of a house and outbuilding in preparation for renovations, and a lorry load of it was dumped in a nearby field. The weather was hard and the pastures bare and the two cows ate a very considerable quantity of it. They showed symptoms closely resembling those of milk fever, with a staggering gait, almost reeling over as they walked, there was some excitement and they occasionally bellowed loudly as if in pain. There was a strong odour of crushed ivy leaves, both in the breath and in the milk, which persisted for about three days. Recovery was complete and uneventful.

UMBELLIFERAE

The Umbellates are one of the largest botanical families. Over three dozen genera are natives of Britian and many others have been imported. The great majority of the family are harmless, and of the many cultivated species, carrots, parsnips, celery and parsley, are a few examples. The poisonous ones are Hemlock, Cowbane or Water Hemlock and Water Dropwort, while a few others such as Fool's Parsley, Water Parsnip, Asses' Parsley and Wild Carrot are suspects.

HEMLOCK (*Conium maculatum* L.)

Countless generations of young people received their earliest lesson in toxicology when they first heard the ancient Greek legend of Prometheus who, after bringing fire to the mortals in a hemlock stalk, was condemned by the gods to eternal punishment, and hemlock was doomed to kill all mortal creatures which ate it. Thus, from earliest times the poisonous nature of hemlock was impressed upon the minds of children. It formed the chief ingredient of the poison cup administered to Socrates, and throughout the ages, its toxicity has been exploited for homicidal purposes. The Anglo-Saxons are known to have used it in their medicines, and its use was again revived in Britain during the latter half of the eighteenth century. Medicinal preparations of the plant are no longer used, however, owing to the uncertainty of their action.

Hemlock is an annual or a biennial—more commonly the latter. It may be found almost anywhere in Britain growing on waste land, hedge-banks, road verges and near streams. The stems are round, smooth and rather shiny, and are thickly covered with purplish spots. The large compound leaves are smooth and hairless and are divided into numerous deeply cut segments. The umbels have about ten to fifteen rays and appear small, compared with the size of the plant, which may attain a height of 5 feet or more.

Hemlock may be distinguished from other members of the family by the smooth, spotted stem and the distinct odour of mice, which all parts of the plant emit when bruised or crushed.

The active principles are several alkaloids, all of which are extremely poisonous and act in a similar manner on the body. They paralyse the respiratory nerves and the victim dies of suffocation.

The most important of the alkaloids is coniine, which occurs in the largest amounts; it is particularly interesting because it was the first alkaloid to be produced synthetically in the laboratory. The others, no less poisonous but occurring in smaller amounts, are methylconiine, coniceine, and conhydrine.

The alkaloids are volatile liquids and are lost by slow drying or boiling, so that matured hay which contains hemlock is not likely to be dangerous to livestock.

All parts of the plant contain the alkaloids, the roots at all times containing the least. In the young plant, the leaves contain the most, but this passes to the fruits or 'seeds' as they form and they are at their most dangerous state when still green but fully formed, i.e., about three-quarters ripe.

Fatal cases of accidental hemlock poisoning in human beings have been due to mistaking the leaves for those of parsley, and the fruits for those of anise. In one instance the plant was actually growing in the middle of a bed of parsley. Illness among people who had eaten quails which had fed upon hemlock seeds has been reported from North Africa.

The unpleasant mousy odour of hemlock is not attractive to animals. Poisoning of livestock is seen mostly in spring, when pastures are short and the young leaves are growing among the more luxuriant grasses of the sheltered hedge-banks and sides of ditches, although at this period of the year they are at their least poisonous stage. Cornevin (1893) states that the fatal dose for the horse is between 4 and 5 lb of the fresh plant, and, for cattle, 9–11 lb.

The main symptoms of hemlock poisoning are similar in all animals. They are dilation of the pupils, rapid respiration, difficulty in movement, particularly of the hind limbs, the pulse, at first slow, becomes rapid and thready, temperature is lowered, there is stupor but not necessarily loss of consciousness. Death follows from respiratory failure, the result of paralysis. The heart may remain beating after breathing has ceased.

In the author's experience, animals which have survived for eight hours after the onset of symptoms, have recovered comparatively quickly, but one in-foal mare and several in-calf cows aborted within a few days.

The alkaloids are excreted by the lungs and kidneys, and the typical mousy odour in the breath and urine of a poisoned animal is diagnostic.

Post-mortem examination reveals parts of the plant in the stomach, the contents of which are permeated with the typical odour. There are no inflammatory changes in the alimentary tract, and other findings are those which one would expect from respiratory arrest; the blood is almost black, the consistency of tar; the liver dark and congested; the right side of the heart full and the left side empty. The lungs are congested and dark coloured and often bear a lighter coloured imprint of the ribs.

First-aid treatment is as follows. Give stimulants, alcohol (brandy, whisky, gin, beer, etc.), and coffee or tea in large quantities. Purgatives should only be prescribed by the medical attendant or the veterinary surgeon, who may also administer such other alkaloids as strychnine or atropine, if necessary, and give oxygen by inhalation or subcutaneously. Artificial respiration may be used in man and in the smaller animals.

COWBANE, Water Hemlock (*Cicuta virosa* L.)

Cowbane is extremely poisonous to man and all classes of livestock. It may be found in such wet places as the edges of lakes, ponds and ditches, from southern Scotland southwards. Its distribution is very local and it is never abundant. The stem is stout, hollow, and furrowed, it is somewhat branched and grows to a height of 3 or 4 feet. The leaves are compound, with long narrow segments which have a few unequal, acutely pointed teeth on their borders. The umbels of white flowers are from 3–5 inches in diameter and contain ten to fifteen or more rays. The rootstock is short, fleshy and hollow, and has a sweetish taste. It has been eaten by human beings in mistake for parsnips, with fatal results.

The active principle is a resinous substance, cicutoxin, which is found in the yellow juice of the roots and in smaller quantities in the stems. It is present in its greatest amount between late autumn and early spring. Its action on the body is that of a convulsant poison.

Small quantities of the fresh root are sufficient to cause death, a piece the size of a walnut being considered a fatal dose for horses and cattle (Nicholson).

Cowbane roots may be dug out and left lying on the surface after cleaning out ditches. As the poison persists in the dried plant, it may cause the death of an animal long after it has been unearthed. The leaves and stems are poisonous, but to a less extent, and they may be eaten when grass is short.

Symptoms of cowbane poisoning in man and animals are similar. There is nausea, widely dilated pupils, vomiting where possible, delirium, violent convulsions and death from asphyxia. There is no purging or diarrhoea.

Post-mortem examination reveals nothing diagnostic, except parts of the plant in the stomach contents.

First-aid treatment consists of keeping the patient warm and avoiding any excitement. Medical and veterinary treatments follow similar lines; they may consist of stomach lavage and attempts to control the convulsions by intravenous injections of the soluble barbiturates or other anti-convulsants.

WATER DROPWORT (*Oenanthe crocata* L.) (Plate III)

Water Dropwort is also called water hemlock in some parts of the country, but it is more widely distributed and more abundant than cowbane. It is found in ditches, slow watercourses, marshes, and similar wet places throughout England and in the south of Scotland. Water dropwort is a stout perennial plant: the branched stem, which is hollow and grooved, stands between 3 and 5 feet high. The leaves are compound and much divided, the segments being more than ½ inch long and deeply cut into three or five lobes; they have been mistaken for those of celery. The white flowers are seen in June and July, and occur in terminal compound umbels with twelve to forty rays, 2 or more inches long, the component umbellules appearing to be almost globular. The description given to the author by a small boy was; ‘It is a stem with a lot of gongsticks stuck around the top’. The rootstock is formed of thick whitish or pale yellow tubers and the name ‘Dead Men’s Fingers’, by which they are known in some localities, is quite an apt description of their appearance. The tuberous roots, the stem, and the leaves, all contain a juice which turns yellow on exposure to the air.

The active principle, oenanthetoxin, has an action similar to that of cicutoxin. It is a convulsant poison which is not affected by drying and storage. Man and all the domestic animals are susceptible to its effects. Fatal human cases of poisoning have occurred when the leaves of water dropwort have been mistaken for those of celery, and the tuberous roots for parsnips. The roots are the most toxic part of the plant and very small amounts are sufficient to cause the death of animals. Poisoning of farm stock usually occurs from eating roots which have been brought to the surface during ditching or drainage operations. Death is rapid and few symptoms may be seen before it occurs. Horses and cattle show salivation, dilated pupils and spasmodic convulsions; they usually die in a convulsion. Sheep are less susceptible to its effects than other animals, and in the author's experience at least fifty per cent of them recover from acute poisoning. It may be worthy of note that on one occasion the author administered chloroform to fifteen sheep in order to control the muscular spasms of the limbs sufficiently long to give intravenous injections of nembutal. Sheep, which have recovered from the acute symptoms, suffer from diarrhoea for about two days and then slowly return to normal. Pigs which have eaten the roots of water dropwort, may vomit for a short time, but death is usually sudden without the appearance of any symptoms. Post-mortem findings and first-aid treatment are similar to those given under cowbane.

Other species of *Oenanthe*, including *O. fistulosa* L. and *O. aquatica* (L.) Poir. are also poisonous but to a lesser degree than *O. crocata*. Several of them, which are reported as causing human and animal poisoning in other countries, have caused symptoms of a depressive type, more reminiscent of hemlock poisoning rather than the convulsive symptoms of cowbane poisoning.

FOOL'S PARSLEY OR Lesser Hemlock (*Aethusa cynapium* L.)

Fool's Parsley is a weed of pastures, waste-land, and gardens; it seldom grows to a height of more than 2 feet. Its chief interest as a poisonous plant arises from the many cases of human poisoning which have occurred through mistaking the leaves for those of parsley, and the roots for radishes. Fool's parsley contains two alkaloids, coniine and cynapine. The poisonous substances do not withstand drying and long storage; hay containing large quantities of the dried plant is harmless to livestock. Animals do not eat the plant in the fresh state, and in pastures where it abounds, even if almost bare of grass, fool's parsley remains untouched. The plant emits a repulsive odour, which becomes more marked when crushed or bruised. This, together with its white flowers and partial involucres of two or three long bracts, should be sufficient to distinguish it from parsley, which has light coloured leaves and yellow flowers, and from radishes which have broad leaves with stout hairs and a single white or light mauve, four-petalled, cross-like flower (*Cruciferae*).

WATER PARSNIP (*Sium latifolium* L.)

Water Parsnip is said to have caused the death of cows, and to taint milk.

THE CHERVILS (*Chaerophyllum* and *Anthriscus* spp.)

The Chervils are believed to have caused the death of pigs and cows, and, to taint the milk of the latter.

Little definite or authentic has been written concerning the poisoning of livestock by these other plants of the hemlock family. They must be borne in mind, however, when searching for the causal plants of poisoning of obscure origin.

In the author's own experience of poisoning by British umbellates any animal which has survived for more than eight hours after the commencement of symptoms has made a successful recovery.

For further reading

HEMLOCK

J. M. BUCHANAN, 1936, *Vet. J.* **92.** 226–7.
J. L. BUCKINGHAM, 1936, *Vet. J.* **92.** 301–2.
B. COPITHORNE, 1937, *Vet. Rec.* **49.** 1018–9.
H. MACDONALD, 1937, *Vet. Rec.* **49.** 1211–2.

Flesh of quails

E. SERGENT, 1948, *Arch., Inst. Pasteur, Algér.* **26.** 249–52.

CUCURBITACEAE

BRYONY, White Bryony (*Bryonia dioica* Jacq.)

Bryony is the sole representative of the Gourd family found wild in Britain. It is one of the best-known hedge climbers of the English countryside, and has been introduced locally in southern Scotland. The name Bryony should not be confused with Black Bryony (*Tamus communis*) which belongs to another family—*Dioscoreaceae.* The rootstock is perennial, large and tuberous 'sometimes nearly 2 feet long, thick as a man's arm, white, succulent and fleshy, with an acid, bitter, and disagreeable taste' (Henslow). The stems are annual and grow to great length, climbing in hedges or other trees and shrubs by means of spirally-twisted tendrils. The leaves are deeply divided into five or seven lobes, the central one longer than the others. The whole plant is covered with minute hairs. The flowers appear in June and July; they are dioecious and of a pale yellowish-green colour, the males being slightly larger than the females. The fruit is a red berry which contains several flat seeds.

The active principle is a glycoside—bryonin—which is a drastic purgative. It somewhat resembles in composition and action the better known purgatives, jalap and colocynth, which are used medicinally.

The whole plant contains an acrid milky juice with an unpleasant odour; it is particularly nauseous when dried and is irritant if applied to the skin.

Cornevin says that the roots have caused poisoning in human beings who have eaten them in mistake for parsnips or turnips, and, in France, where it is known as 'Devil's turnip', many accidents have occurred among women at the time of weaning their infants because of the popular belief that it will diminish milk secretion. The berries are also poisonous and Cornevin estimated that forty were sufficient to cause the death of an adult and that fifteen would prove fatal for a child.

Poisoning of domesticated animals by bryony is not often seen; but pigs may root out and eat the rootstock, and poultry may eat the berries, with fatal results. The author has known cases where cattle have been poisoned by the rootstocks of bryony when, during early spring, they were dug out and left on the surface of a pasture after excavations had been made for a pipeline. The operation had entailed the removal of about 60 yards of an old hedge in which bryony had grown luxuriantly for many years without causing harm. Neither owner nor workmen recognized the roots for what they were nor had they any idea that they were poisonous. Forty milking cows were turned into the field on the morning after the excavations had been filled in, and by afternoon, four were found lying down in a state of collapse, their bodies were cold and their eyes deeply sunk in their sockets. Treatment with stimulants proved of no avail and all died quietly in a coma within an hour of being found.

Post-mortem examination revealed large quantities of the chewed fleshy root in the rumen, the walls of the rumen were inflamed and the lining membranes were more easily detached than usual. No other pathological changes of note were observed. Two other cows showed symptoms of grunting and cessation of rumination, followed by a profuse watery diarrhoea; they recovered in a few days after appropriate symptomatic treatment. It was computed at the time that none of those which died had eaten less than 4 lb of the root. It is noteworthy that the two recovered animals acquired a craving for bryony, and during the following summer they searched the hedgerows for it and ate leaves, stems, and flowers, whenever they were available. This caused attacks of acute indigestion and diarrhoea with almost complete, but temporary, cessation of milk secretion.

Horses have been poisoned by eating the stems and leaves. They show symptoms of copious urination, sweating, tetanic convulsions, stupor and super-purgation, or complete suppression of defaecation.

First-aid treatment must be symptomatic and is similar to the treatment of any case where there has been overdosing with purgatives. Warmth, quietness, and administration of stimulants are necessary, together with liquids to make up for body fluid lost from the diarrhoea.

EUPHORBIACEAE

The great majority of the native species, and a large number of exotic ones in the Spurge family, are poisonous. They include the Spurges (*Euphorbia* spp.) Dog's Mercury (*Mercurialis perennis* L.), Annual Mercury (*M. annua* L.), as well as the exotic Castor Oil bean (*Ricinus*) which occasionally causes poisoning of livestock when included in other foods. Most of them are irritants and drastic purgatives similar in action to croton and jalap, which are obtained from exotic plants of the family.

SPURGES (*Euphorbia* spp.)

The Spurges are weeds, some of them are extremely common, while others have only a very local distribution in the southern counties of England. Poisoning by them is very uncommon in Britain, and there are very few recorded instances. Reports from America and Australia have mostly concerned the poisoning of cattle by the Caper Spurge (*Euphorbia lathyrus* L.) which is a weed of woodlands in the south of England, and is sometimes found established in old gardens; a relic from former cultivation. It is a tall, stout herbaceous annual or biennial (usually the latter) standing 3 or more feet high. It is a smooth, glaucous plant with leaves in pairs, opposite on the stems in contradistinction to most other species in the genus, which have alternate leaves. The stem leaves are narrow, the upper ones being broader at the base and longer than those lower down; they are often 3 or 4 inches long. The upper part of the stem terminates in an umbel of three or four long rays, which themselves branch or fork once or twice to carry large ovate-lanceolate floral leaves and flowers. The fruits are large, smooth, lobed capsules, each with a single wrinkled seed, resembling capers in appearance.

SUN SPURGE (*E. helioscopia* L.)

Sun Spurge is much more common than the caper spurge. It is an annual weed of cultivated ground and may be seen in fields and in gardens throughout the country. It is an erect, golden-green coloured annual from 6 to 18 inches in height; with a simple stem, or a few weak branches which ascend from the base. The few stem leaves are arranged spirally and are spatulate or spoon-shaped, being broader at the tip than at the base. The upper five leaves, which are minutely toothed at their edge, are in a whorl around the stem which divides above them into an umbel of five rays. Each of these rays forks once or twice at the ends to carry floral leaves and flowers in crowded clusters. The flowers are in the leafy head and are unisexual; a solitary female stands on a short stalk bent downwards away from the several male flowers which surround her. They are seen from early summer to late autumn. The fruit is a smooth capsule of three lobes, each lobe containing a single seed which appears to be closely pitted all over its surface.

DWARF SPURGE (*E. exigua* L.)

Dwarf Spurge is a weed of cornfields and cultivated places. It is very variable in height—anything from 1 or 2 inches to nearly 1 foot, but seldom more. There may be several slender branches from the base, and the stem leaves are smaller, narrower and more numerous than those of the sun spurge. The umbels are of three or four rays with greenish flowers which appear from June to October. The fruit capsule is warted at the angles of the three lobes and contains three slightly wrinkled seeds.

PETTY SPURGE (*E. peplus* L.)

Petty Spurge is a small annual, branching on short stems from the base. It is about 6–12 inches high, light green in colour, with smooth, light green, broadly ovate leaves. The umbel of two or three rays, which repeatedly fork to carry the floral leaves and flower-heads, occupies the greater part of the plant. The fruit capsule has three carpels, each with a longitudinal rib or narrow wing and containing a single, pitted seed.

POISONING BY SPURGES

All the spurges contain an abundance of milky juice, which is a severe irritant if applied to the skin or tissues. The active principle is believed to be a complex substance, euphorbiosteroid, of which little is known. The milky juice is an irritant poison, and the oil contained in the seeds is a drastic purgative. The activity of neither is affected by drying and storage, and this should be kept in mind if dried fodder crops containing large quanitities of any of the spurges are fed to animals.

In Ireland, the juice of the Irish spurge (*E. hiberna* L.) is used as a fish poison, and in Africa several species are gathered by the various tribes and used in the preparation of their arrow-poisons.

The caper spurge has been grown in gardens and used in the preparation of purgative medicines in the past. The taking of these medicines often resulted in such drastic effects that their use has long been discontinued. It has been eaten with boiled mutton, either in mistake or as a substitute for capers and the effects were those of an irritant poison. Young cattle have been affected by it in America and in Australia.

The petty spurge, sometimes known as 'milk-weed', has caused illness and losses among horses and cattle in Australia and of sheep in New Zealand.

The sun spurge has been commonly gathered by generations of children, who dress warts on their fingers with the milky juice. If they suck their fingers afterwards there is intense irritation of the lips and tongue, accompanied by an acute burning sensation. It is from this use and its juice that it receives such local names as 'wolf's milk', 'cat's milk', 'wart-wort' and 'wart-weed'.

On one occasion the author examined a flock of about forty lambs suspected by the owner to be suffering from 'orf', a disease caused by a filtrable virus. They had been folded for two days on a very weedy field of marrowstem kale which had been a failure. By far the most predominant weed was sun spurge, which was as high as the kale and much more plentiful. It appeared that if a lamb were to eat kale he would also have to eat some of the spurge. All the lambs were affected to a greater or less degree; the lips, dental pads and tongues were swollen and inflamed and the tips of the tongues of those worst affected were abraded by the incisor teeth. There was copious salivation and some diarrhoea, but the latter was not excessive. They were removed to a good permanent pasture and had fully recovered after two days, without other treatment. This is the only instance within the author's knowledge of animals eating any of the spurges, or of their causing illness of livestock in Britain.

Mercurialis spp.

This genus has only two species—Dog's Mercury (*Mercurialis perennis* L.) and Annual Mercury (*M. annua* L.).

DOG'S MERCURY (*Mercurialis perennis* L.) (Plate V)

Dog's Mercury is a weed of woods and shady places and is found throughout Britain. It is a rough or hairy perennial with a slender creeping rootstock. The stems are erect and not branched, and stand 6 inches to 1 foot high. The leaves are oblong or ovate-lanceolate, pointed at the tip, serrated at the edges, and are 2–5 inches long. They are slightly hairy on both sides, on short stalks, opposite on the stems, and crowded on the upper half of the plant. The flowers are dioecious. They are on peduncles which are as long as the leaves or longer. The male flowers are in little clusters on the peduncle, and the females, singly or two together. They are green in colour and appear early in spring before the leaves are fully out. The fruit is a two-lobed capsule, which is covered with bristly hairs or soft prickles and contains two warted seeds.

ANNUAL MERCURY (*Mercurialis annua* L.)

Annual Mercury is an erect, hairless annual 6 inches to 1 foot high, with opposite branches. The leaves are ovate or oblong on short stalks with rather coarse teeth around the margin. They are thinner and of a finer texture than those of dog's mercury. The male flowers are on long peduncles, like those of dog's mercury, but the females are found in the axils of the leaves. The flowers are green and may be seen during the whole summer and until late autumn. The plant may be found in fields, gardens and wasteland in England, but it is not so common as dog's mercury. It occurs casually in Scotland and Ireland.

Both plants are very poisonous if eaten by livestock, and human poisoning has occurred from eating them as a vegetable. (The toxin was one of the panaceas of the old herbalists and quacks, and no doubt hastened the end of many of their patients.) These plants contain a volatile basic oil, mercurialine, which is responsible for at least a part of their toxicity.

Both dog's mercury and annual mercury cause acute illness of cattle and the highly irritant poisons severely injure the stomach, bowels and kidneys. The animal may live for several weeks in a comatose or semi-comatose condition.

Polidori and Maggi (1954) found experimentally that acute poisoning of cattle by *M. annua* only followed the feeding of plants with seeds, those which had lost their seeds being apparently harmless. The feeding of dried plants and seeds produced a chronic form of poisoning in rabbits.

Symptoms are gastro-enteritis, primary constipation followed by foetid or bloody diarrhoea, cessation of milk secretion, blood-stained urine, rise in temperature, and coma leading to death.

Post-mortem appearances are acute gastro-enteritis, sometimes with loss of the intestinal mucous membrane. The liver shows cloudy swelling or fatty degeneration, and there are haemorrhagic infarcts in the kidneys. Natale (1946) says, that in Italy the carcass meat from animals slaughtered while ill from poisoning by these plants, if well bled, is considered to be safe for human food, but that all the offals are condemned.

First-aid treatment. Give bicarbonate of soda in large doses, followed by eggs, milk, and sugar, to soothe the irritation.

CASTOR OIL PLANT (*Ricinus communis* L.)

The Castor Oil plant is grown in Britain only as an ornamental plant. The seeds, however, are imported for the extracting or pressing of castor oil, which is used both medicinally and for lubrication. The press-cake from crushing the seeds or beans as they are commonly called, is as poisonous as the beans themselves. Large numbers of animals have died from the admixture of cake or of the beans with other foodstuffs. All types of animals are susceptible to its effect.

The poisonous principle is a phyto-toxin called ricin, of which only infinitesimal amounts are required to kill. It is a true toxin, similar in many respects to those elaborated by bacteria, but it differs from most bacterial toxins and snake venoms by its ability to pass through the bowel wall into the blood-stream. The blood reacts to it by forming antibodies, similar to the antibodies formed during bacterial disease, and in this way an immunity to its effects can be created. A specific anti-serum may be obtained for the treatment of poisoned animals or for protection against poisoning. It is obtained from animals which have been slowly 'hyper-immunized' by giving them the toxin, starting with doses too small to cause clinical symptoms and gradually increasing them until they are receiving amounts many times greater than would be required to cause the death of an untreated animal. Experiments carried out in Norway have shown that immunity to the effects of the bean can also be produced in animals by feeding on graduated amounts of it.

Biological tests carried out in the laboratory can confirm or negative the presence of ricin in an animal's body or in foodstuffs. These tests are conducted in a manner similar to those used for the diagnosis of many bacterial diseases.

According to Clarke (1947), the susceptibility to poisoning by ricin of the different farm animals is in the following order: horses, sheep, cattle, pigs, ducks and poultry. Several days usually elapse between the eating of the contaminated food and the appearance of symptoms. Symptoms are progressive, becoming more serious as the case goes on. McCunn, Andrew, and Clough (1945) describe the following symptoms of ricin poisoning in working horses: profuse sweating, straggling, rocky gait, temperature slightly raised, tetanic spasms in muscles, tumultuous heart and pulse, visible mucous membranes dark and injected, absence of throat lesions, diarrhoea without blood in faeces. Recovery was slow if the purging was delayed.

Post-mortem examination revealed semi-fluid or fluid contents of the alimentary tract, patchy inflammatory condition of the mucous membranes of the bowels, oedema and cloudy swelling of liver, kidneys, and spleen, oedema of lungs, trachea and bronchi filled with frothy oedematous fluid, right side of heart engorged, oedema of bronchial, mesenteric, and hepatic, lymph nodes.

For further reading

PETTY SPURGE

A. E. A. SHARAF, 1948, *Vet. J.* **104.** 313–8.
1949, *Brit. vet. J.* **105.** 128–35.

CAPER SPURGE

H. A. BAYLEY, 1941, *N.Z. J. Agric.* **63.** 327.

DOG'S MERCURY

G. EATON, 1941, *Vet. Rec.* **53.** 145.

MERCURIALIS SPP.

P. TROCHRIE, 1948, *Alfort Thesis.*

ANNUAL MERCURY

A. ROMAGNOLI, 1935, *Nuova Vet.* **13.** 36–8.
A. ZINGHI, 1936, *Nuova Vet.* **14.** 252–4.
N. S. BARON, 1944, *Vet. Rec.* **56.** 513
K. DIERNHOFER and A. KMENT, 1943, *Wien tierärztl. Wschr.* Sept 17th, 316–9 Oct 1st, 331–8.
K. LOHWAG, 1947, *Wien tierärztl. Mschr.* **34.** 665–9
L. NATALE, 1946, *Zooprofilassi* **1.** (5) 15–8.
F. POLIDORI and M. MAGGI, 1954, *Nuova Vet.* **30.** 146–50

CASTOR SEEDS

Camel

E. F. PECK, 1942, *Vet. Rec.* **54.** 184.
A. S. LEESE, 1942, *Vet. Rec.*, **54.** 246.

Horses

SCHMIDT, 1942, *Z. Veterinärk.* **55.** 337. *Abst.* in **70.** 531. *Jber. Vet. Med.* 1943.
J. MCCUNN, H. ANDREW and G. W. CLOUGH, 1945, *Vet. J.* **101.** 136–8.
E. G. C. CLARKE, 1947, *Vet. J.* **103.** 273–8.

Cattle

T. S. ANDERSON, 1948, *Vet. Rec.* **60.** 28.
T. GEARY, 1950, *Vet. Rec.* **62.** 472–3.

Serum

E. G. C. CLARKE and J. H. JACKSON, 1956, *Brit. Vet. J.* **112.** 57–62.

POLYGONACEAE

Docks and Sorrels are the best-known wild plants in the Polygonum family, which also includes the Rhubarb of our gardens, and Buckwheat, which is at times cultivated on British farms as a grain crop.

(132217) G

SORREL, Common Sorrel, Sour Sorrel, Sour Dock (*Rumex acetosa* L.)

Sorrel is a perennial; it has a thickish rootstock and an erect furrowed stem, which shows little branching. It stands 1–2 feet high and is a common weed of fields, gardens, and waste places. The leaves are mostly radical, they are from 3 to 5 inches long, bright green in colour, and tend to rectangular shape, with the base like an arrow head (sagittate). There are only a few stem leaves, the lower ones being on short stalks, and the upper sessile and appearing to grip the stem. The flowers are dioecious, or occasionally monoecious, in long leafless terminal panicles, which are at first green, but later turn red.

SHEEP'S SORREL, Sour Grass (*Rumex acetosella* L.)

Sheep's Sorrel is a common weed of pastures throughout Britain. In general appearance it is reminiscent of a miniature common sorrel, and stands between 4 inches and 1 foot in height. It is a perennial with red or red and green stems, the leaves are mostly lanceolate, but a few of them are arrow-shaped. The flowers, like those of common sorrel, are mostly dioecious and the panicles turn red.

The taste of the leaves and stems of both common sorrel and sheeps' sorrel, is extremely acid, due to the large amount of oxalic acid and soluble oxalates they contain. The leaves of common sorrel were used in many home-made remedies of the past, and are still included in salads by many people.

Livestock eat small quantities of both plants without harm, but if they are forced to eat them in large amounts, or over a long period, the effects are similar to those caused by the other plants which contain oxalates.

Sheep, particularly lactating ewes, are more commonly affected by them than are cattle, but both plants have long been considered by farmers to be a contributory cause of milk fever in both animals. This is understandable when one considers that the presence of a large amount of either of the sorrels in a pasture is indicative of lime deficiency of the soil, and that 'milk fever', as generally understood in these animals, is due to a deficiency of calcium in the body. Animals which graze for a long period on lime-deficient pastures soon lose their body reserves of calcium and their blood is deficient or near-deficient in this essential mineral, particularly if they are in milk at the time. It does not require much imagination to visualize that if an extra drain is placed on the remaining calcium of the blood—as actually happens when the oxalates from such plants as the sorrels combine with it and are excreted by the kidneys—then symptoms of calcium deficiency will develop. These will be similar in every respect to milk fever. Cases of poisoning of ewes by common sorrel have been reported from Canterbury, New Zealand (1937), and from England by Coward (1949). The symptoms recorded by both writers were almost identical, and were similar to those seen in milk fever and to those of poisoning by oxalates from other sources. The Canterbury ewes were suckling lambs from five to eight weeks old and 90 per cent of them recovered after treatment by calcium injection (Connor, 1951). Symptoms of poisoning by sorrels in sheep are staggering, great prostration—affected animals may lie on their sides and become tympanitic (blown)—followed by coma and death. The incidence of this type of disease has been considerably reduced in Britain in recent years by the revival of the practice of liming agricultural land.

Post-mortem examination alone is not diagnostic; a slight gastritis may be the only lesion, and the blood may show some loss of its clotting powers. Blood analysis may show the presence of oxalates and calcium deficiency.

First-aid treatment. Give draughts of chalk and water to prevent further absorption of oxalates. Animals which are uneasy on their legs or staggering should receive injections of calcium borogluconate as soon as possible.

Prevention of poisoning by sorrel is similar to that described for mangolds and sugar beet (see page 52). Chalk distributed in blocks or licks about the pastures will go far towards rendering the ingestion of the plants quite safe.

RHUBARB (*Rheum rhaponticum* L.)

Rhubarb is grown in almost every garden, the thick leaf stalks are edible and are usually eaten cooked with sugar as a dessert or boiled to make conserve. The green leaves are definitely harmful if eaten by man or animals. Cases of human poisoning by rhubarb leaves, cooked like spinach, have occurred in Europe. The symptoms have been nausea, violent emesis, diarrhoea and impaired clotting of the blood.

Pigs and goats are the animals most likely to be affected by rhubarb leaves in Britain and, as the active principles are oxalic acid and the soluble oxalates, the symptoms and treatment are similar to those described above.

Polygonum spp.

Several species of the Polygonum genus have been recorded as having caused gastro-enteritis in animals that have eaten large quantities of them. They include: Water Pepper or Smartweed (*Polygonum hydropiper* L.), Knotgrass, Knotweed or Wireweed (*P. aviculare* L.) and Persicaria, Peachwort, or Redshanks (*P. persicaria* L.). The reports come from Europe, America and Australasia, but there are no records of their having caused poisoning of livestock in Britain. All these plants are known to contain a sharp acrid juice, which is extremely irritant if applied to the skin, and there is no doubt that if they were eaten in any quantity they would cause a severe irritation or inflammation of the stomach and bowels. Under British conditions of grazing, however, animals avoid these plants, and poisoning by them is not very likely to occur.

BUCKWHEAT (*Fagopyrum esculentum* Moench.) syn. (*Fagopyrum sagittatum* Gilib.; *Polygonum fagopyrum* L.)

Buckwheat is occasionally cultivated on British farms as a fodder crop, but it is not so widely grown as in many parts of Europe and America, where buckwheat flour is the main ingredient of a popular type of pancake. The black pyramidal grain is harmless at all times and is used as a stockfeed. It is imported into Britain and mixed with other seeds in many cage-bird and poultry mixtures. The growing plant and the straw which remains after threshing are commonly fed to animals and give rise to the condition known as fagopyrism.

Fagopyrism was the earliest recognized form of photo-sensitization (see page 8) and affects animals which are exposed to strong light. Animals which are housed and those with heavily pigmented skins do not develop the disease, but animals with white or lightly pigmented areas are readily affected. It takes the form of an acute dermatitis, the skin of the non-pigmented parts dying off, leaving raw, slow-healing patches. Jaundice is an almost constant symptom, and it may be seen either before or immediately after the appearance of dermatitis.

Within a few hours of gaining access to a field of unripe buckwheat, turkeys, in France, became incoordinate and developed intense pruritis with vesication on the bare parts of the head. The birds were treated with promethazine hydrochloride and lesions regressed after thirty-six hours.

Animals to which buckwheat straw or the green plant are being fed should always be housed and kept out of the sunshine. It should be given only to those with heavily pigmented skins; black-and-white and white cattle and pigs are particularly susceptible to this condition.

First-aid treatment. Immediately house affected animals in a dark place. Treat the skin with emollients containing animal fats rather than petroleum bases and give large quantities of sugar and eggs internally. Because of the jaundice, oily purgatives are definitely contra-indicated.

For further reading

SORREL

Agric. Bull. Canterbury Chamber of Commerce, 1937. **96.**
T. G. COWARD, 1949, *Vet. Rec.* **61.** 765–6.

BUCKWHEAT

M. M. PRIOUZEAU, 1942, *Rec. Méd. vét.* **118.** 160–8.

CANNABIACEAE

HEMP, Indian Hemp, Marijuana (*Cannabis sativa* L.)

Hemp is a tall, erect, dioecious annual which may stand from 5 to 8 feet (1·5–2·5m) in height. The leaves are slender and are palmately divided into five to seven long narrow lobes with serrate margins. Like those of the hop, a better-known member of the same family, they are rough to the touch and have a feel somewhat reminiscent of sand paper. The flowers are green and inconspicuous and are borne on the upper portions of the stems which exude a sticky resinous substance. The fruit is an achene which is commonly sold as 'hemp seed' for inclusion in bird-seed mixtures or for oil pressing. Although widely grown as a commercial crop in many of the warmer parts of the world, it does not necessarily need a tropical or sub-tropical climate and it may be found occasionally growing wild, and usually unrecognized, in England, around rubbish dumps and places where seed mixtures, in which attempts to render them infertile have not proved completely successful, have been fed to wild birds.

Hemp is probably one of the very earliest known narcotics and is reputed to have been used for that purpose by the Assyrians many centuries B.C. It has long been used in human and veterinary medicine as a hypnotic or sedative but in latter years, although its medicinal use has been largely superseded, it has become a drug of addiction among certain of the less responsible members of society.

The active principles, of which a gum-resin, cannabinol, is perhaps the best known, are to be found in the leaves of the growing plant, in greater concentration in the unfertilized female flowers and the maximum in the resinous exudate from the stems. The fruits are harmless. When grown for drug production, rather than for fibre and seed, the male plants are pulled up and discarded as soon as they can be distinguished.

The drug is smuggled out of producing countries in several forms: 'ganja' (compressed flowering tops), 'bhang' or 'dagga' (leaves and flowering shoots together), and 'charas' (the collected resinous substance from the stems). The two first are in demand for mixing with tobacco and smoking in cigarettes (reefers) and the last for inclusion in sweetmeats and drinks (hashish). The odour of the burning dried plant is distinctive. Unauthorized possession of hemp in any of its forms is illegal in all Western countries.

FAGACEAE

OAK (*Quercus* L.)

There are two native oak trees in Britain (*Quercus robur* L. syn. *Q. pedunculata* Ehrh. and *Q. petraea* (Mattuschka) Liebl. syn. *Q. sessiliflora* Salisb.). The former is a gnarled, spreading tree found on clay soils and is the Common Oak of the greater part of England and southern Scotland. It has sessile or short petioled glabrous leaves.

The latter is a less-spreading tree with a straight trunk and stalked leaves which have stellate hairs on the underside. It is the oak of light and shallow soils and is found particularly in the north and west of the British Isles.

Where they occur together there are many intermediates, and other species of exotic origin are naturalized in plantations and gardens. Some, like the Holm Oak (*Quercus ilex* L.), are more or less evergreen; others are little more than shrubs.

In all of the oaks the flowers are monoecious, the males in slender pendulous catkins and the females solitary or clustered, each one surrounded by an involucre of small scales. The fruit or acorn is ovoid and protrudes from a woody cup formed from the scales.

The poisonous qualities of oak leaves and acorns for cattle and sheep have been recognized from the earliest times. Poisoning by the green leaves is usually seen in spring, when if pastures are short they sometimes eat the buds and young leaves from low-growing branches. Much more frequently, however, poisoning occurs in the autumn, when cattle eat fallen acorns and oak leaves from under the trees. Young cattle are reputed to be more susceptible to this form of poisoning than older animals, but in the author's experience, dairy cows and outlying dry cows are quite commonly affected.

Cows may be poisoned by acorns and oak leaves several times in the same season. Once they have been affected by them, however slightly or acutely, they acquire a craving for them. Unless care is taken to keep convalescent cattle indoors for a long period, or to pasture them in fields with stout fences, they will attempt to go back to the trees, and by breaking fences or going through hedges may severely injure themselves. Sheep are seldom or never affected at this season; their grazing habits differ, and they do not usually eat any quantity of fallen acorns or leaves. Wagner (1935) describes how a flock of two hundred sheep ate green acorns and suffered from typical acorn poisoning. Eight of them died within a few hours, and others which were ill, recovered.

Occasionally, pigs have been poisoned by excessive quantities of acorns, but such an occurrence is very rare. Pigs usually thrive on them, and many farmers turn pigs into the pastures and woods where acorns abound, to eat them as they fall. In many parts of Europe, particularly Germany, acorns are gathered and dried. They are ground into a meal which is used in combination with other foods for pig feeding; it is reputed to impart a much-esteemed flavour to the flesh. Indigestion or poisoning of pigs, turned out to eat acorns, is much less likely to occur if other foodstuffs are given as well. It is common practice to house these animals at night, giving them a small feed before they go out and another on their return.

Oak contains a large amount of tannic acid or tannin, particularly in the bark; it is also present in the leaves and acorns. It is undetermined whether the tannic acid alone is responsible for poisoning cattle, or whether there are other unknown substances which may cause some of the symptoms. Tannic acid or tannin acts as an astringent when applied to tissues, and coagulates blood and proteins. The latter property has been known for thousands of years—ever since leather was first made by tanning skins and hides with oak bark.

The ingestion of small quantities of acorns and oak leaves may cause no symptoms at all or a mild form of indigestion which passes off again in a day, without treatment. Acorn and oak leaf poisoning of cattle, however, is clinically a separate entity, and no one knows exactly the conditions necessary, either in the animal or in the acorn, for them to set up poisoning. There may even be an interval of several days between the eating of them and the occurrence of symptoms.

Symptoms are progressive, beginning with cessation of rumination and lack of appetite; the animal refuses to drink, after primary constipation dark-coloured faeces are passed in small quantities and in the later stages may be accompanied by a little blood. The temperature remains normal or sub-normal, the pulse is weak and respiration laboured. The mucous membranes are pale, and there may be a watery discharge from the eyes, nose and mouth, although the muzzle is dry. Milk of lactating animals is bitter and unusable for any purpose. Urine is dark-coloured and is passed frequently and in small quantities. In the more chronic type of case, there is considerable wasting, the animal apparently drawing on its body reserves. Cases which are likely to prove fatal show aggravated symptoms, with flatulence and abdominal pain, and death may occur suddenly during a convulsion.

Buffalo and cows in Bulgaria which ate oak buds and young leaves had typical symptoms of poisoning, with the addition of oedema of the lower parts of the body, oedema of the lungs, and catarrhal pneumonia. The milk of affected animals had a bitter taste (Angeloff and Thomoff, 1938).

Post-mortem examination reveals acute enteritis, as from other irritants. The rumen and reticulum may be normal but in cases in which death has supervened after an illness of two days, the abomasum may be inflamed. The kidneys show some inflammatory changes and small haemorrhages. There may be excessive fluid in the serous cavities, pleura, pericardium, and peritoneum, which is occasionally blood-stained.

First-aid treatment. Give eggs and skimmed milk in large quantities to neutralize the effects of the tannic acid, add sugar as a stimulant; as the micro-organisms of the rumen are reduced by tannic acid, give baker's yeast on the second day. Liquid paraffin may be given as a laxative, with milk, mucilage and stimulants. Saline purgatives such as Epsom and glauber salts, or anthracenes as aloes should not be given under any circumstances.

The convalescence of recovered animals may be slow and protracted, and careful nursing is required. It must not be forgotten that the milk of lactating animals which have eaten oak leaves or acorns has an extremely astringent and bitter taste. Even a small amount added to a churn may render all the milk in the churn unsaleable. On more than one occasion the author has seen such milk refused by hungry calves.

For further reading

OAK

Cattle and Sheep

I. B. BOUGHTON and W. T. HARDY, 1936, *J. Amer. vet. med. Ass.* **89.** 157–62.
C. BJANKOFF, 1938, *Vet. Sbir.* **42.** 73–8. (Summary in German.)
F. BOKO, 1938, *Jugosl. vet. Glasn.* **18.** 339–41.
S. ANGELOFF and Z. THOMOFF, 1938, *Rep. 13th Int. vet. Congress.* **1.** 306–15 and 318.

Acorn Poisoning

I. B. BOUGHTON, 1943, *Tex. vet. Bull.* **5.** No. 4. 2–3.
K. G. TOWERS, 1950, *Vet. Rec.* **62.** 74–5.
E. G. C. CLARKE and E. COTCHIN, 1956, *Brit. Vet. J.* **112.** 135–9.

ERICACEAE

None of our native species of the Heath family are known to cause poisoning. Many ornamental shrubs of exotic origin are grown in gardens and shrubberies, and the best known of them is the Common Rhododendron which now grows almost wild in many parts of the country. The rhododendrons and their cousins the azaleas and kalmias are poisonous to livestock.

COMMON OR PONTIC RHODODENDRON (*Rhododendron ponticum* L.)

The Common or Pontic Rhododendron is a much-branched evergreen shrub, with hard, dark green, entire leaves, about 4–5 inches long, smooth and glabrous but not particularly shiny. The flowers appear in spring and their purple racemes of funnel-shaped corollas are well known. Species other than *R. ponticum* are cultivated in gardens, the colours of the flowers varying from white to darkest purple or deepest maroon.

All the rhododendrons grown in this country are poisonous to livestock. They contain a neutral principle—andromedo-toxin—which is also present in azaleas and kalmias.

Honey gathered from the flowers of rhododendron may be poisonous, but as it is used up by the bees themselves almost immediately during spring, and honey is seldom taken from the hives at that time of year, chances of poisoning from this source are remote.

Poisoning may occur in all classes of livestock which have access to garden refuse and clippings, and when, by way of broken fences or carelessly opened gates, they gain admission to gardens and shrubberies.

Symptoms of poisoning are similar in all animals—salivation, distressing attempts to vomit, colic, slow and difficult breathing, staggering gait, great debility and death from failure of respiration.

The horse, in his futile attempts to vomit almost screams and becomes very distressed; of two horses, seen by the author, one collapsed and died in a few hours, the other recovered slowly in a few days but was not fit for work for a further week. Sheep, like horses, make a considerable amount of noise in their retchings and are not very productive of vomitus. Cattle vomit more easily than sheep, and when they do so, may project the vomit for a considerable distance. In one shed where eight dairy cows were poisoned the author saw the walls on the far side of the feeding passage covered with vomited ingesta, and his own goat, which had eaten rhododendron clippings, projected her vomit for over eight feet.

Post-mortem examination reveals the presence of the leaves in the stomach. There is little, if any, inflammation, the vomiting being caused by the action of the poison on the nerve endings in the stomach walls.

First-aid treatment consists of keeping the animal quiet and warm. The administration of stimulants is necessary, but is difficult to accomplish by drenching and may cause the suffocation of an animal which is continuously retching. Alcohol is the stimulant most easily available, and diluted brandy, whisky or gin, may be given as early as possible. The veterinary surgeon may administer other medicaments by the stomach tube or hypodermically.

For further reading

RHODODENDRON

Cattle

J. W. H. MASHETER, 1941, *Vet. J.* **97**. 223–5.

PRIMULACEAE

SOWBREAD or Common Cyclamen (*Cyclamen hederifolium* Ait., syn. *C. europaeum* auct.)

Sowbread contains the glycoside, cyclamin.

COMMON or SCARLET PIMPERNEL (*Anagallis arvensis* L.)

Common Pimpernel contains the glycoside, smilacin.

Both glycosides are a variety of saponin which, if taken in sufficient quantity, causes poisoning of the same type as that caused by corn cockle. It is not likely that animals would eat sufficient of either plant to cause poisoning under normal British conditions but in Northern Iraq the author examined a number of horses and mules which were suffering from severe anaemia and debility from this cause. Examination of blood showed no evidence of parasites, the number of red corpuscles was reduced and a large percentage of those present showed crenellation.

The animals were much thinner than they should have been on the amount of grain allowed to them and stood about, listless and almost continually yawning, moving only when forced to do so. Closer examination showed extreme pallor of visible mucous membranes, weak but rapid pulse, shallow respiration and low temperature. Faeces varied from normal to loose but there was no diarrhoea. The only sign which gave any indication as to the possible cause of the condition was the large heap of dark coloured froth which formed during micturition. This rose to about the height of the animals' hocks and persisted for eight or more minutes.

Owing to lack of rain at the proper season, the barley straw, which formed the main bulk of their diet, was extremely short and, in order to obtain sufficient fodder to carry over the dry season, the ground had been almost shaved by hand. This had resulted in the inclusion of a large crop of pimpernel which, in the dry state, the author could not distinguish from *A. arvensis* and which would most certainly have been missed had the normal harvesting machinery been employed.

Treatment consisted of a change of straw, injections of cyanacobalamin, iron tonics with trace elements and vitamin B complex in the form of the local bread ferment. There was no death among treated animals and recovery, although slow, was complete.

OLEACEAE

The British representatives of the Olive family are the Ash tree (*Fraxinus excelsior* L.), Lilac (*Syringa vulgaris* L.), and Privet (*Ligustrum vulgare* L.).

ASH TREE (*Fraxinus excelsior* L.)

The Ash is a strikingly handsome tree, being tall, with spreading branches. The leaves are deciduous and pinnate, with seven to thirteen ovate segments which are toothed along the borders. The fruits are winged samaras, commonly known as 'keys', and are about 1½ inches long.

The keys and leaves of the ash are not known to contain large amounts of poisonous substances, but they give rise to acute impaction of the rumen, should cattle eat large quantities of fallen leaves in the autumn. The condition is known in the Midlands as 'Wood Evil'.

Symptoms are those of acute indigestion, the passage of small quantities of hard faeces, or complete cessation of defaecation, grunting, cessation of rumination and fall in milk yield. The rumen contents, when felt through the left flank, are found to be impacted into a solid mass. Temperature rises to about 103·5°F. Affected animals eat nothing and drink very little.

Since this is a condition of the rumen in which the balance of the normal flora is disturbed, it is necessary to encourage rumination by stimulating fermentation and replacing the micro-organisms. Bakers' yeast is most suitable for this purpose. The author has on several occasions resorted to rumenotomy when the rumen contents have been tightly impacted and medicinal treatment has proved valueless in breaking down the mass.

COMMON PRIVET (*Ligustrum vulgare* L.)

Common Privet, and an introduced species Oval-leaved Privet (*L. ovalifolium* Hassk.) which is now more commonly planted for hedges, are shrubs with long slender branches, and grow from 6–10 feet high. The leaves are on short stalks, ovoid and opposite, and are very nearly evergreen. The flowers are white and small, and they are seen in July and August in compact panicles at the end of the branches. The fruit is a black globular berry, divided into two cells with one or two seeds in each.

The active principle of privet is a glycoside, ligustrin, of which little is known.

Children have been fatally poisoned by eating the berries. They showed symptoms of drowsiness, difficulty in movement, severe vomiting and purging.

Because of its toxicity, privet is seldom used as a hedge plant where animals have access to it. Horses are more likely to eat it than most other animals, although the author's goat ate considerable quantities, without apparent harm.

The author made post-mortem examinations of two horses which had died of privet poisoning on consecutive days, both belonging to the same owner. Each had been allowed to browse on a privet hedge while the driver ate his lunch. The hedge had long been neglected and was in flower. The first horse showed symptoms of slight colic and unsteady gait while still on the road; he was walked slowly home and died on his return to the stable, about four hours after eating the plant. The second horse showed similar symptoms and died on the road. Post-mortem examination showed that over half of the stomach contents of each horse consisted of privet leaves and flowers. The walls of the stomach were acutely congested but there was no other condition worthy of note.

The cases recorded by Turner (1904) did not die for thirty-six to forty-eight hours, after symptoms of loss of power in the hind-quarters, slight increase of temperature, and dilated pupils.

For further reading

PRIVET

Cattle

1939, *N.Z. J. Agric.* **59.** 430.

BORAGINACEAE

The Borage family is a large one and includes such well-known plants as Alkanet, Forget-Me-Not, Comfrey, Bugloss, Borage and Heliotrope. Few species are considered to be very poisonous, although, in Australia and New Zealand, Heliotrope (*Heliotropium europaeum*) and in Australia, Purple Vipers Bugloss (*Echium lycopsis* L. syn. *E. plantagineum* L.) are both held responsible for causing 'heliotrope poisoning', a syndrome of toxic liver cirrhosis which is indistinguishable from seneciosis or ragwort poisoning.

Greatorex (1966) described the poisoning of a herd of twenty-three cows by Hound's-tongue (*Cynoglossum officinale* L.). They all showed signs of having ingested an irritant poison, with incoordination, tympany, rapid pulse, dyspnoea and dark green diarrhoea as prominent symptoms. Four animals died and the remainder recovered completely within five days after symptomatic treatment. Post-mortem examination of the four which died revealed large quantities of Hound's-tongue leaves in the rumen with inflammation of the walls of all stomach compartments and congestion of the lungs.

For further reading

E. LYCOPSIS

T. D. St. George-Grambauer and R. Rac, 1962, *Aust. Vet. J.* **38.** 288–93.

C. OFFICINALE

J. C. Greatorex, 1966, *Vet. Rec.* **78.** 726–7.

CONVOLVULACEAE

LARGE DODDER (*Cuscuta europaea* L.)

Large Dodder is a slender twining annual parasite which is reddish in colour and twists in an anti-clockwise direction. In Britain it is found chiefly on nettles and hops to which it attaches by suckers. In Russia, horses and cattle fed upon hay which contained 60 per cent of Large Dodder suffered from chronic ulcerative enteritis which, in some instances, proved fatal. Horses given 2·5 kg. chopped dodder daily showed colic between the 20th and 25th days of feeding and died after 30 to 40 days. A similar syndrome seen in Uzbekistan was found to be caused by *Cuscuta breviflora*.

SOLANACEAE

All native and most cultivated members of the Solanum or Nightshade family are poisonous. The family includes thorn-apple, henbane, woody, garden, and deadly nightshades, potato, tomato and tobacco.

THORN-APPLE (*Datura stramonium* L.)

Thorn-apple is a coarse glabrous branched annual 1–2 feet high, with large ovate leaves which are irregularly lobed with pointed teeth. The flowers are single, have a sickly scent and are seen during July and August on short stalks which arise from the middle of the forks. The green calyx is about 1½ inches long with five teeth or lobes. The corolla is funnel shaped, about twice as long as the calyx and bordered with five pointed teeth. It is usually white, but sometimes it is violet or purple. The capsule, which contains numerous wrinkled black seeds, is ovoid or globular, with four valves, and it is very prickly—hence the name thorn-apple.

Thorn-apple is seen only in southern England, where a taller species, the entire-leaved thorn-apple (*D. metel* L.) is also sometimes found. Both species are introductions.

All parts of the plant, the seeds most especially, are poisonous and contain the alkaloids atropine, hyoscyamine, and hyoscine. If eaten in hay or in the fresh state, it induces symptoms similar to those caused by the deadly nightshade.

HENBANE (*Hyoscyamus niger* L.) (Plate V)

Henbane is a coarse erect annual or biennial, hairy all over, and with an unpleasant odour; it stands about 1–2 feet high. The coarsely-lobed radical leaves are large and on short stalks. The stem-leaves are alternate, unevenly lobed and sessile, the upper ones clasping the stem. The lower flowers are on short stalks in the forks of the branches, the upper flowers have no stalks and grow on one side of a leafy shoot. While flowering, the calyx is comparatively short, but it continues to grow and protect the fruit, when it is then about 1 inch long and strongly veined. The points of the five lobes harden into spine-like prickles. The corolla is funnel shaped and five lobed, a little over 1 inch long and about 1 inch across. It is yellowish-white at its borders with purple veining and a central purple 'eye'. There are five stamens with purple anthers. The fruit is a globular capsule enclosed in the ribbed calyx, the upper part, when ripe, splitting off transversely like a cap, to expose numerous seeds.

All parts of the plant, including the seeds, are very poisonous, and the active principles are chiefly the alkaloid, hyoscyamine, with smaller amounts of hyoscine and atropine. They are not destroyed by drying and storage and are not affected by boiling. Poisoning effects are similar to those produced by deadly nightshade. It is reputed to impart an unpleasant taste and odour to the milk of cows which eat it. This must, however, be of extremely rare occurrence, owing to the habitat of the plant and its nauseating odour. It may, on rare occasions, be included in roadside hay.

Henbane is not a common plant, it is only found occasionally in waste places, around old villages, and in the vicinity of ruined castles and monasteries, and where it has spread from the gardens in which it was formerly cultivated for medicinal use. The root is large and thick and is more poisonous than the other parts of the plant; it has been eaten, with serious results, in mistake for parsnips and chicory.

DEADLY NIGHTSHADE, Dwale, Belladonna, Banewort, etc. (*Atropa belladonna* L.) (Plate IV)

Deadly Nightshade is not so widely known as is sometimes believed, many people attributing the name 'deadly nightshade' to the bittersweet or woody nightshade which is almost ubiquitous in its distribution. The deadly nightshade, like henbane and thorn-apple, is more commonly seen in the southern counties than elsewhere and is very local in distribution; it is found usually in similar places and, at times, side by side with the other two plants.

It is a branched herbaceous plant standing 2–5 feet high, with a thick fleshy perennial rootstock and erect branching annual stems. The leaves are large, ovate and entire, and occur on short stalks in pairs on one side of the stem, one leaf of the pair being usually more than twice the size of the other. The solitary flowers droop on short stalks which arise from the leaf axils or forks of the stems. They appear in July and August. The calyx is broadly campanulate and has five triangular lobes. The corolla is bell-shaped, nearly 1 inch long with five broad short lobes; it is a dull, pale, purplish-blue which appears almost as if the colour has faded. The fruit is a berry which, when ripe, is purplish-black in colour; it is round and slightly flattened, and the calyx is persistent and spreads open.

Poisoning may occur in man and animals from eating all parts of the plant, but animals seldom touch it. Children and young animals are more susceptible to its effects than adults, and the author has seen deaths among calves from eating the leaves and stems. The most poisonous parts are the roots and seeds, although the stems, leaves and flowers contain large quantities of the poison. The berries are attractive to children, who may mistake them for black cherries; one berry is known to have caused severe illness and three, the death of a child. The plant is cultivated for medicinal purposes, and extracts prepared from it are used in ointments, plasters, and liniments.

The active principle is chiefly the alkaloid, hyoscyamine. This is the alkaloid which occurs in the largest amounts in thorn-apple, henbane and deadly nightshade. Atropine, if it occurs at all in the growing plants, does so only in very small quantities. It is prepared commercially for medical use from hyoscyamine obtained from the entire-leaved thorn-apple (*Datura metel* L.).

Hyoscine, sometimes called scopolamine, is also found in the growing plants in smaller amounts; it is less toxic than hyoscyamine and is used medicinally as a narcotic.

Taken by mouth or instilled onto the surface of the eyeball, all of these alkaloids cause dilation of the pupils of the eye. They are excreted from the body by the kidneys and can be recovered from the urine by analysis. A test which is applied for diagnosis in cases of suspected poisoning by these plants is the instillation of a few drops of the patient's urine into one eye of a healthy animal and after half an hour, exposing it to bright light. In positive cases the pupil of the treated eye will be fully dilated, while the opposite eye will react normally. The household cat may be used for this purpose because the pupils are more easily seen and compared than those of most other animals. It will suffer at the most only slight inconvenience and no pain.

Rabbits are reputed to be able to eat large quantities of deadly nightshade without harm to themselves, but their flesh, if eaten by human beings, gives rise to symptoms of poisoning similar in every way to those which occur from eating the plant itself. It is very probable that the flesh of other poisoned animals, which may be slaughtered in emergency, is poisonous in the same way, but no definite proof of this is forthcoming.

Human symptoms are: dryness of the mouth and throat, impaired vision, dilation of the pupils, loud heart-beats which may be heard several feet away, hallucinations, delirium, sleepiness and coma. Death may follow from heart or respiratory failure.

Man is apparently more susceptible to the effects of these poisons than the domesticated animals, except perhaps the dog and cat; they do not eat the plant but may be poisoned by medicinal preparations. The pig, sheep and goat may eat comparatively large amounts of these plants without visible harm. Horses and cattle are more susceptible, but have a greater power of resistance to them than has the human subject.

In experimentally feeding seeds of *Datura stramonium* to cattle and pigs, Hesselbarth (1962) found that cattle are able to tolerate amounts up to 7 gm of the seeds daily (approximately 17 mgm hyoscyamine), while pigs tolerate up to 5 gm daily (approximately 14 mgm hyoscyamine). The author made post-mortem examinations of three calves about six months old, which had strayed and were found dead in the derelict garden of a tumble-down cottage. Deadly nightshade was growing in the garden and showed signs of having been eaten. Parts of the leaves and stems were recovered from the rumen, and urine taken from the bladder of one of them caused dilation of the pupil of a cat and of a cow. There were no lesions which indicated any reason for death, other than asphyxia from nightshade poisoning.

Symptoms in animals are dry mouth, incoordinated movements, dilation of the pupils, loud respiration and heart-beats, inability to rise when down, stupor, convulsions and death. Salivation has been seen in poisoning by henbane.

Post-mortem examination reveals part of the plant in the stomach or bowels and signs of respiratory failure. There are no inflammatory changes. Betts (1938) found a large clot of blood around the kidneys, caused by dilation and rupture of blood vessels in that region.

First-aid treatment. To children give an emetic immediately, preferably mustard and water, followed by stimulants such as strong coffee or tea. Medical advice should be sought immediately and acted upon with all possible care.

To animals which can vomit give an emetic; to the others, strong coffee or tea in large quantities, and alcohol. Veterinary treatment may consist of attempts to wash out plant parts from the stomach and the administration of morphine, caffeine, eserin or pilocarpine, as requisite. As far as possible, animals should be kept moving about until otherwise advised.

THE GENUS SOLANUM

This genus includes Woody Nightshade or Bittersweet (*Solanum dulcamara* L.), Black or Garden Nightshade (*S. nigrum* L.), and the Potato (*S. tuberosum* L.); the Tomato (*Lycopersicum esculentum* Mill.) is included here for convenience.

WOODY NIGHTSHADE, Bittersweet (*Solanum dulcamara* L.)

Woody Nightshade is also erroneously called 'deadly nightshade' in some parts of the country.

It is not so commonly seen in Scotland as in England and Wales, where it enjoys a much wider distribution than any of the other wild species of the Solanum family. It is found in damp and shady places, and its slim branches and pretty flowers are frequently seen climbing and trailing over shrubs and hedges along the roads. The roots are perennial and the stems are woody at the base; they branch and straggle untidily and are often many feet long, dying far back during winter. The leaves are dark green on short stalks and alternate on the stems. The lower ones are three lobed and ovate, the centre lobe being by far the largest. The upper leaves are ovate and entire, heart-shaped at the base and pointed at the apex.

The flowers are seen from June to September in small cymes. They are very small, about ½ inch in diameter. The anthers form a bright yellow cone around the style, and the bright purple corolla has five lobes, which are inclined to turn back towards the stalk. Except for the colour, the flower of the woody nightshade is reminiscent of the tomato flower. The fruit is a small egg-shaped or globular red berry.

Children may be attracted to the berries, and cases of poisoning by them are known. Animals do not readily eat the plant, but if cattle acquire the taste for it, which they occasionally do, they will go to endless trouble to satisfy their craving. The juice of the stem and leaves is intensely bitter when first tasted, but it leaves a sweet taste in the mouth afterwards. It is from this property that it gained its name 'bittersweet'.

All parts of the plant contain large quantities of solanine and its allied alkaloids. Symptoms of poisoning are in all respects similar to those described on page 92, except perhaps that dilation of the pupils is more often seen in poisoning by nightshade.

BLACK, OR GARDEN NIGHTSHADE (*Solanum nigrum* L.) (Plate IV)

The Black, or Garden Nightshade is a weed of almost world-wide distribution. It is known all over England, particularly in the south, where it is often a troublesome weed of gardens. In Scotland, its distribution is very local and it grows only where it has been introduced by cultivation.

It is an erect annual or biennial herbaceous plant which grows to about 1 foot in height. The stem is very branched and is glabrous or only very slightly hairy. The leaves are stalked and ovate, either entire or with coarse angular teeth, and alternate on the stems. The flowers are small and white, they droop downwards in small umbel-like clusters and they close at night.

They are seen during summer and autumn, the anthers form a small cone in the centre of the corolla which has five triangular lobes; these are slightly hairy and at the margins are inclined to turn back towards the stalk.

The fruits are berries which contain numerous seeds. They are usually black when ripe but some forms, probably always introduced, have red or persistently green berries.

Another species (*Solanum sarrachoides* Sendtn.) which somewhat resembles *S. nigrum*, is sometimes found in East Anglia and occasionally elsewhere. It differs from the latter species in being more densely hairy and in the calyx which becomes considerably enlarged by the time the fruit has ripened. The fruit remains green when mature.

Wherever *S. nigrum* or *S. sarrachoides* occur in fields, great care must always be taken to ensure that the green fruits are not included in such crops as peas for processing.

Like the other species of the genus, black nightshade contains solanine and its allied alkaloids. The quantity of the poisons in the plant varies with soil, climate, and season. In some districts it is reputed to be harmless, and deadly in others. Conflicting reports of its toxicity and of its harmless nature are inclined to mislead the unwary. Cattle have died from eating the plant in New Zealand and America, and children have suffered in varying degrees, from a slight 'collywobble' to acute illness and death, as the result of eating the berries.

The variation in the poison content of individual plants and differences in conditions of growth makes it very necessary to warn children against eating the plant and berries.

Symptoms of poisoning of animals are similar to those described for solanine poisoning (page 92).

POTATO (*Solanum tuberosum* L.) and TOMATO (*Lycopersicum esculentum* Mill.)

There is no need to describe either the Potato or the Tomato. But it is less well known or seldom recognized, however, that they are the products of two poisonous plants.

The stems and leaves of both potato and tomato plants contain a series of alkaloidal glycosides known as 'solanines'. Of these, solanine and solanein are always present, and solanidine (a decomposition product of solanine) may accompany them. All of them are insoluble in water and withstand ordinary cooking or boiling. Their action on the body is in many ways similar to that of the saponins which cause haemolysis of the blood, if taken regularly in small doses; in many European countries, the feeding of large quantities of well stored potatoes to young cattle over long periods is a well recognized cause of severe chronic anaemia. In larger doses there is depression, loss of appetite, great prostration, with gastritis and blood-stained urine, and stupor; a total indifference to the surroundings is a common feature. The tuber of the potato is the commonest source of the poison in man and among the domesticated animals in this country, but the feeding of green potato haulms to animals has caused great losses in Europe.

The author has seen acute illness and death of pigs from eating green tomato plants on two occasions, when the sideshoots, which are picked out regularly by growers, were collected together and tipped into a pig trough.

The tuber of the potato, when exposed to the light becomes green. During this 'greening' process large quantities of solanine are produced and render the green parts extremely poisonous. The 'eyes', skin and young sprouts, if green, are most dangerous. Fatality in human beings and innumerable instances of severe illness have been reported from all over the world, after people have eaten greened or sprouted potatoes. Few house-wives, unless in dire necessity, will trouble to cook potatoes of this type, because of their bitter, unpleasant taste. Potatoes which have become green by exposure to light but are otherwise sound, are said to be safe for pig-feeding after adequate boiling. When required for feeding to cattle, or when boiling is not practicable, they can be rendered wholesome again by storage, in total darkness or in a clamp for a fortnight or more, until all trace of green coloration has disappeared from under the skin.

The author makes no apology for including the following old doggerel rule for feeding potatoes: the advice is sound even though the rhyme is poor:

> When potatoes, leaves, or haulms are green,
> To livestock must they ne'er be gi'en.

SOLANINE POISONING

The symptoms seen in animals are great prostration, drowsiness and total indifference to environment. Pigs, if lifted, will stand for a short time and either lie or fall down again; they seldom squeal if handled, the body temperature is low, and if there is copious dark-coloured diarrhoea, the chances of survival are fairly good. Dilation of the pupils may or may not be seen, and if it occurs it is not diagnostic of solanine poisoning. Pigs which recover often suffer from dermatitis for a time afterwards. Cattle become dull and lie more or less continuously; they refuse, or are unable, to rise, rumination ceases, the muzzle is dry and the extremities cold. There is little rise in temperature and the animal is quiet, making no sound, except perhaps, in acute cases, from laboured respiration. Dark-coloured diarrhoea, as with pigs, may follow initial constipation, and when this supervenes the chance of survival improves.

Cases have been reported of poisoning of horses. They showed considerable weakness and loss of power of the limbs as the most constant symptoms. Poultry are also affected by solanine.

Post-mortem examination of animals which have died from poisoning by any of the plants which contain solanine, reveals little but evidence of slight gastro-enteritis; the kidneys may appear congested and the bladder may or may not contain blood-stained urine. The presence of parts of the plants or pieces of potato tuber is helpful. In these cases, the stomach contents often feel 'soapy' on the rubber glove.

First-aid treatment of animals suspected to be suffering from solanine poisoning is a matter of general stimulation, and for this purpose in the early stages large quantities of warm, strong tea, well sweetened with sugar, is of great help.

GENUS NICOTIANA: TOBACCO (*Nicotiana tabacum* L.)

Tobacco is not a native of Britain, but because of the heavy rate of duty levied upon imported leaves, it is now being grown here in increasing amounts in gardens and allotments.

Tobacco is the source of a volatile liquid alkaloid—nicotine. In the pure state, nicotine is colourless but it turns brown after exposure to the air. It is extremely poisonous and can easily be absorbed through unbroken skin or a raw surface, and very small doses may cause death. Without expert analysis, it is impossible to assess the nicotine content of the dried leaves or of the fresh plant; many samples of 'mild' tobacco have a greater nicotine content than some of the 'strong' ones. In Britain, preparations of tobacco and nicotine have been used in agriculture and horticulture as pesticides, and from these sources arise the largest number of cases of poisoning, both human and animal. Occasionally, tobacco and nicotine have been given internally to animals as a medicament for worms. Rose (1936) computed that the mortality in lambs was 8·4 per cent, when a nicotine-copper sulphate mixture was used in Australia. A mixture of nicotine and lime, applied to the backs of cattle as a dressing for the larvae of the warble fly, has set up poisoning. Sometimes, tobacco leaves are applied to wounds and tobacco poultices to boils; such medicaments are extremely dangerous, as are washes made from tobacco for the treatment of mange and lice. The author saw a horse with a large open wound which the owner had dusted with snuff 'to keep off the flies'. Within half an hour of the application the symptoms were alarming. After profuse sweating and salivation, followed by a convulsion, the animal became cold and in a state of near-collapse, the pulse rapid but weak, and respiration fast but shallow. Recovery followed treatment with strong, hot tea and sugar given by stomach tube, and hypodermic injections of camphor in ether. The wound was washed with soap and water and the surface scraped with a sharp knife.

The author made post-mortem examinations of two fat pigs which, after having broken loose from their sty in a garden, ate a large quantity of growing tobacco plants. They were driven back to their sty in apparently good health, but were found dead four hours later. The stomachs were about half full of the plants and there were no lesions or indications of any other cause of death.

For further reading

THORN-APPLE

N. D. KEHAR and K. G. RAV, 1944, *Indian J. vet. Sci.* **14.** 112–4.
HESSELBARTH, 1962, *Prakt. Tierärztl* No. **7**: 266–7.
Ibid No. **8.** 304–5.

DEADLY NIGHTSHADE

R. S. BETTS, 1938, *J. Amer. vet. med. Ass.* **93.** 45.

Pigs

J. C. HUBBS, 1947, *Vet. Med.* **42.** 428–9.

BLACK OR GARDEN NIGHTSHADE

Cattle

W. G. BONNER, 1938, *N.Z. J. Agric.* **57.** 99–101.

Goats

O. V. GUNNING, 1949, *Brit. vet. J.* **105.** 473–4.

WOODY NIGHTSHADE

Horses

O. GESSNER, 1943, *Berl. Münch. tierärztl. Wschr.* **7/8.** 47–8.

POTATO, LEAVES AND TUBERS

N. A. SOSHESTVENSKII, 1939, *Sovetsk. Vet.* (3) 81–3.

Cattle

J. B. MILLIGAN, 1941, *Vet. Rec.* **53.** 512.

Horses

O. V. GUNNING, 1950, *Brit. vet. J.* **106.** 32–3.

Solanine

L. H. Lampitt, J. H. Bushill, H. S. Rooke and E. M. Jackson, 1943, *J. Soc. chem. Ind., Lond.* **62.** 20–4. 48–51.

M. Steffens, 1943, *Berl. Münch. tierärtzl. Wschr.* Sept. 3rd, 302–3.

D. D. Ogilvie, 1943, *Vet. Rec.* **55.** 288.

Fowls

H. Temperton, 1943, *Vet. Rec.* **55.** 359.

Pigs

W. J. Ironside, 1943, *Vet. Rec.* **55.** 268.

SCROPHULARIACEAE

The Scrophularia family includes the Foxglove (*Digitalis purpurea* L.), Mulleins (*Verbascum* spp.), Toad flax (*Linaria* spp.), Figworts (*Scrophularia* spp.), Lousewort (*Pedicularis* spp.), Yellow Rattle (*Rhinanthus* spp.), and Cow-wheat (*Melampyrum* spp.), all of which are known to contain sufficient poisonous glycosides to cause the acute illness or death of any animals which eat a quantity of them. That few recorded cases of poisoning by the growing plant in man or animals are to be found in either medical or veterinary literature of the last fifty years, is due to several factors, the most important of these being that animals will not eat them.

Foxgloves and mulleins remain untouched by stock even when brought to near-starvation at times when pastures are bare and practically everything else which is green has been stripped from the banks and hedges. Farmers, knowing them to be dangerous to their stock, take care not to include them in hay, and treat the presence of toad-flax, yellow rattle and cow-wheat as signs of poor husbandry. Children are warned, and not unwisely so, at an early age by parents, teachers and other children, of the dangers of playing with foxgloves, and these warnings, coupled with the unpleasant taste, prevent what might be serious consequences.

FOXGLOVE, Dead Men's Bells (*Digitalis purpurea* L.) (Plate VIII)

Foxglove is usually a biennial, but sometimes forms a rootstock which flowers for two or three years. The radical leaves are on long stalks, ovate or ovate-lanceolate in shape, about 6 inches or more in length, toothed at the margins and coarsely veined; the under-surface is covered with a soft white down. The flowering stem stands up to about 4 or more feet high and has a few alternate and shortly-stalked leaves. The upper part is occupied by a long handsome raceme of purple flowers, each about 1½ inches long. The inside of the corolla is hairy and beautifully spotted. Occasionally a white variety is seen wild or cultivated in gardens.

The leaves of the foxglove are used in medicine; they are dried and powdered and are then known as digitalis. The whole plant contains a series of glycosides, the most important in the wild plant being digitoxin. These glycosides have an effect upon the muscles of the heart, and in large doses are liable to cause cessation of the heart-beat. The dried plant, if taken in large doses, is liable to cause irritation of the stomach and bowels and frequent attempts at urination which, in the early stages, may be copious but later becomes scanty. The effect on the heart is similar to that caused by the glycoside. Drying and storage or boiling does not reduce the toxicity, and hay containing dried foxgloves has caused poisoning in horses and cattle.

Parker (1951) has described poisoning of sixty-eight young turkeys from eating the growing leaves of foxgloves. The chief symptoms were drowsiness, inappetence, stasis of the crop, and dilation of the pupils. Ten died, and in these, convulsions were observed immediately prior to death. The remainder recovered after the surgical removal of the crop contents.

Post-mortem examination reveals parts of the plant in the stomach and occasionally, slight gastro-enteritis.

First-aid treatment must consist of demulcents, e.g., milk and eggs or linseed tea, with purgatives to follow. Atropine may be administered later if the medical attendant or veterinary surgeon considers it necessary to steady the heart action.

WATER FIGWORT (*Scrophularia aquatica* L.)

Water Figwort is an erect perennial up to about 3–4 feet high. The stem is quadrangular, the angles projecting into narrow wings, the leaves are opposite on the stems, ovate, and serrated at the margins. The flowers are seen during the whole summer; they occur in a long narrow panicle and are of a dull purple colour. The plant has an unpleasant odour. It is found in wet ditches or at the sides of streams in England but is rare in Scotland.

Ewart (1937) has described poisoning with water figwort in young cows. The symptoms were excitement, accelerated and short respirations, dilated pupils, congestion of mucous membranes of gums and mouth with slight ulceration, infrequent and painful urination, profuse dark foetid diarrhoea, great thirst, but lack of appetite, and diminished milk secretion.

After treatment with tannic acid, saline purges and stimulants, they recovered completely in two days.

OTHER SCROPHULARIACEAE

Little is known of the clinical aspects of poisoning by most of the other poisonous plants of this family. From knowledge of their glycoside content it is extremely likely that poisoning would take the form of violent purging and symptoms similar to those described by Ewart. Poisoning by them is unlikely because of their unpleasant odour and taste, but it may occur in unusual circumstances.

For further reading

FOXGLOVE

Turkeys

W. H. PARKER, 1951, *Vet. Rec.* **63.** 416.

WATER FIGWORT

Cattle

R. H. EWART, 1937, *Vet. Rec.* **49.** 1514.

OROBANCHACEAE

BROOMRAPE (*Orobanche* spp.)

There are a number of species of broomrape to be found in Britain, all of them are parasitic and none of them contain chlorophyll. They are attached to the host plant by underground tubers from which a scaly flowering stem arises.

The one most likely to cause poisoning of livestock is Lesser Broomrape (*Orobanche minor* L.) because it is commonly parasitic upon *Trifolium* spp. and other leguminous fodder plants. The flowering stem, which carries a few brownish scales, is yellowish, tinged with red, and may stand from 4 to 20 inches (10–50 cm) in height. The flowers are arranged as a spike; looser below and becoming closer towards the apex, they are yellowish in colour and tinged and veined with purple.

Lesser Broomrape has caused gastro-enteritis and diuresis in goats and dogs, Kamel (1956), and on analysis was found to contain tannin, a resin and small amounts of a glycoside.

For further reading

S. H. KAMEL, 1956, *Rev. Elev.* **9.** 43–8.

LABIATAE

GROUND IVY (*Glechoma hederacea* L. syn. *Nepeta hederacea* (L.) Trev.)

Ground ivy has caused poisoning of horses in England and in Europe, with symptoms of pulmonary oedema and enteritis.

For further reading

S. GONDA, 1936, *Allatorv. Közl* **36.** 173.
B. VON HAZSLINSKY, 1935, *Dtsch. tierärztl. Wschr.* **43.** 708–9.
NICOLAU, *et al*, 1956, *Mh. Vet. Med.* **11.** 534–8.

RED HEMP NETTLE (*Galeopsis ladanum* L.)

Red Hemp nettle has caused poisoning of horses in Europe.

Frolkin (1965) states that when *Galeopsis* seeds were fed to horses and pigs for about a week, at a rate of 1·1–2·5 per cent of their diet, four out of eighteen horses and seventy-five out of one hundred and fifty store pigs died in a coma after a period of inappetence.

For further reading

M. FROLKIN, 1965, *Veterinariya*, **42.** No. 9. 68.

HENBIT (*Lamium amplexicaule* L.)

Henbit has caused poisoning of cattle in Queensland, Australia.

For further reading

Qd. Agric. J. 1940, **54.** 242.

LOBELIACEAE

ACRID LOBELIA (*Lobelia urens* L.)

Acrid Lobelia is found wild in a few English counties, but is very local. It is a perennial with a creeping root-stock and oblong radical leaves. The stems are about 1–1½ feet high and bear a few lanceolate slightly toothed leaves in the lower half, and in the upper part a long slender raceme of purplish-blue flowers. The flowers are seen in late summer and autumn.

Acrid Lobelia contains, among other alkaloids, lobeline, an alkaloid which resembles nicotine and coniine in its action.

CAPRIFOLIACEAE

COMMON ELDER (*Sambucus nigra* L.) and DWARF ELDER (*Sambucus ebulus* L.)

These are too common to require description. They have a certain reputation among country people as purgatives when the bark, leaves or berries are eaten. There are few modern records of their having seriously poisoned animals, which, if they eat them at all, do so in moderate amounts.

DIPSACACEAE

DEVIL'S-BIT (*Succisa pratensis* Moench, syn. *Scabiosa succisa* L.)

Devil's-bit was reported over fifty years ago to have caused damage to the tongues of cattle which ate it. There has been no record of it since then.

COMPOSITAE

The Composite family is large and includes many of our best-known garden flowers: chrysanthemums, erigeron, asters and daisies, as well as common weeds like thistles, dandelions and chamomiles. Many British species have been used for medicinal purposes, but very few of them could be classed as poisonous, and none of them are capable of causing sudden death. Members of the genus *Senecio* (groundsels and ragworts) are the only species known to cause poisoning in Britain, but others which grow here are known to have poisoned animals abroad. These include the poisoning of pigs in Esthonia with the Jerusalem Artichoke (*Helianthus tuberosus* L.), the poisoning of cattle in Switzerland with Mugwort (*Artemisia vulgaris* L.) and the poisoning of cattle in Australia and New Zealand with Milk Thistle (*Silybum marianum* L.) Gaertn syn. (*Carduus marianus* L.) and of lambs with the pappus hairs of Stinkwort (*Inula graveolens* (L.) Desf.).

Human poisoning has occurred from over-doses of the oil, or infusions, of Tansy (*Chrysanthemum vulgare* L.) which has been taken medicinally.

Several plants of this family cause an unpleasant taint in the milk of dairy cows.

SENECIO spp.

The genus *Senecio*, so-called because pappus formation cause the seeding flower heads to resemble the grey heads of old men, enjoys wide distribution throughout the world. In Britain, the best known species are the annual groundsels and the biennial or, under certain conditions, perennial ragworts. Of the latter, Common Ragwort (*S. jacobaea* L.) is almost ubiquitous in its distribution. Others, which are far more local, are Marsh Ragwort (*S. aquaticus* Hill), Hoary Ragwort (*S. erucifolius* L.), Oxford Ragwort (*S. squalidus* L.) and Cineraria (*S. cineraria* D.C.).

COMMON RAGWORT, Ben Weed, Curley Doddies (Scots.) (*Senecio jacobaea* L.)

Common ragwort was also known in past ages as St. James's Wort, because it honoured the saint by being in full flower on his day, July 25th, and as Staggerwort from its reputed effect upon horses after they had been fed upon it in hay or in cut green fodder. Herbal preparations of the plant were, at one time, held in great esteem as emmenagogues.

It is a strikingly handsome erect biennial or perennial plant which may stand from 1½–3 feet (0·5–1·0 m) high. The stems are grooved, the lower half appearing red in colour, with the upper half green and branched. The leaves are light green and are deeply dissected and toothed, giving them the ragged appearance from which the name is derived. The flowers are in large brilliant yellow corymbs and are seen everywhere in Britain, on the bombed sites of London, in pastures, in gardens, and on railway and hedge banks. In fact, one may say that wherever there is sunshine, there is ragwort. It is a most troublesome weed to eradicate from pastures. Animals will not normally eat it, consequently it flowers and seeds down undisturbed, until finally, there may appear to be more ragwort than grass. Many authorities have recommended the grazing of such pastures with sheep, which they erroneously believe will eat it off without harm to themselves. This belief has been proved fallacious, both experimentally and on many farms, to the cost of those who have tried it. Sheep will not eat any quantity of ragwort if there is an alternative and, if they do eat much of it for prolonged periods, are just as liable as other animals to suffer from its effects. The effects are not immediate, and when they occur the cause is seldom recognized.

When farmers and those responsible for enforcing measures for its control can be brought to realize that ragwort alone probably causes more annual loss to the livestock industry than all the other poisonous plants put together, then, and only then, will there be any diminution in the enormous quantities which are to be seen in pastures, on roadsides, in publicly owned places and even occasionally in private gardens throughout the country.

Ragworts, groundsels and cineraria in Britain, as well as species of the genera *Crotalaria* (Leguminosae), *Heliotropium* and *Echium* (Boraginaceae) overseas, all contain pyrrolizidine alkaloids which are recognized as being directly hepatotoxic and to be the active principles responsible for that syndrome which culminates in death from toxic cirrhosis of the liver and which is known as ragwort poisoning, seneciosis or seneciasis.

Seneciosis also occurs among human beings in many parts of the world. In South Africa, 'bread disease' occurs among certain native tribes. This is caused by the ingestion of food grains contaminated with the seeds of *Senecio isatadeus* which they have omitted to remove by winnowing, sieving or washing before pounding or grinding it into meal. In Jamaica, 'Bush tea' made from crotalaria has been blamed for a similar disease among children.

Sudden sporadic outbreaks of toxic hepatitis and liver cirrhosis, for which no cause is ever definitely established, occur occasionally among animals in the most unexpected places. Until comparatively recently it has been generally assumed that plants of the genera previously mentioned or their products have been responsible. However, since the effects of aflatoxin, the complex of toxins produced by a mould, *Aspergillus flavus*, have been further investigated another potential source has been revealed by Loosmore *et al.* (1961). It is now certain that, in cattle at least, this complex can produce a syndrome which is indistinguishable both clinically and macroscopically post-mortem from ragwort poisoning, although Hill K. R. (1963) found some cytological differences in liver sections he examined microscopically.

Of six or more active principles present in common ragwort, the hepatotoxic pyrrolizidine alkaloids; jacobine, jacodine and jaconine are the best known. Isatadine has been isolated from *S. isatadeus* and aquaticine from *S. aquaticus*. Each species has one or more alkaloids and, although there are well defined chemical differences which separate and identify them in the laboratory, the effects each of them produces cannot be distinguished in the living animal nor macroscopically during the most careful post-mortem examination. They are cumulative in their effect and are not affected by drying or storage. Silage, hay and artificially dried grass, which contain ragwort, are definitely dangerous and it is from these sources, rather than from the fresh plant, that the vast majority of clinical cases arise. Cockburn *et al.* (1954), describe a case at law, heard in the Queen's Bench Division, in which damages and costs were awarded to the plaintiff for loss of cattle from ragwort poisoning, occasioned by the presence of ragwort in dried grass supplied by the defendants.

The alkaloids act directly upon the abdominal viscera, especially the liver, causing congestion and tiny bleeding spots (petechiae). In most of the other viscera recovery usually occurs without leaving any permanent effect but the damage to the liver is followed by the type of degeneration which is known as cirrhosis. In this condition, after the original damage, which may include occlusion of tiny veins and death of surrounding cells, the liver tissue becomes progressively replaced in part by fibrous tissue. As the disease slowly progresses, the liver function diminishes until, finally, it ceases altogether and the animal dies. The illness and death are thus due to the after-effects rather than to the immediate action of the poison which, at the time of ingestion, may have caused little visible upset or even have passed unnoticed.

After eating the fresh or dried plant, symptoms may be exhibited by animals relatively soon, or may be delayed for several weeks or even months. Similarly, the course of the disease, from the onset of symptoms to death, varies in individual animals; it may be comparatively short, an affected animal dying in from six to ten days, or it may be prolonged, the animal remaining in a gradually declining state of health for weeks or months. Thus, in a group of affected animals, illness and deaths may be spread over a considerable period of time.

The early signs are loss of condition, poor appetite and constipation. As the disease progresses all these become worse, the lining membranes of the mouth, nostrils, and eyelids, become pallid and may show the yellow colouration of jaundice. Diarrhoea is not usual, even in the later stages. Continuous straining is a common symptom in cattle and as a result, eversion of the rectum may occur. In the late stages of the disease the brain may appear to be affected; horses show 'sleepy staggers', while cattle may develop a mania—they become furious and unapproachable. When this occurs liver function is at a low ebb, and death soon follows.

While in Iraq, the author had the almost unique opportunity of observing the whole course of an outbreak of this type of poisoning in a flock of about 140 in-lamb ewes. The plant responsible, the toxicity of which was confirmed by carefully controlled feeding experiments in which lambs from another flock and a different district were used, could not be distinguished from cineraria (*Senecio cineraria* D.C.) by the author nor by the local botanists whom he consulted. Its distribution appeared to be very local and was thought by the botanists to be of comparatively recent introduction. It was found as a perennial weed in and around cornfields and among growing corn in well defined areas. In this instance it had survived the harvesting of a barley crop by combine harvester after which, following local custom, the soil had been left undisturbed for at least a year or even more. When the flock was brought to graze on this land plants of this species formed at least one-third of the vegetation it supported.

The first deaths occurred within a fortnight of the commencement of grazing and were thought by the owner to be the result of rabies, owing to several of the affected ewes having attacked others, the sheep-dog and the shepherd. The author saw none of the aggressive cases while alive but, after rabies had been negatived, post-mortem examinations were made. These revealed, in every case, acute congestive hepatitis with petechial sub-mucous and subserous haemorrhages in most of the abdominal viscera including, and not least, in the uterus. The pasture was changed immediately and barley and barley-straw were given in addition.

Although the owner realized that the remainder of the flock were almost certain to succumb to the disease, he refused, on religious grounds, to slaughter pregnant ewes. Consequently, every one of them was seen before it died and was autopsied afterwards. After the first forty deaths from the acute disease, which occurred within a fortnight of the beginning of the outbreak, no more died for several weeks. Despite good food and every care, the general condition of the flock deteriorated rapidly and, except for the fact that no fluke was ever found and the worm burden was negligible, the overall clinical picture which was presented closely resembled that seen in chronic liver-rot caused by heavy fluke infestation. Some of the ewes soon became grossly emaciated while others held their condition for much longer. Oedematous swellings were commonly seen in the jowl and under the brisket and these not infrequently extended beneath the thorax and abdomen. At post-mortem examination the liver was found to be cirrhotic and shrunken and oedema was usually seen around the vessels of the stomach and bowels but there was no sign of petechiae in the abdominal viscera which had characterized the earlier acute cases.

During the course of the disease no ewe aborted and all had died within four months of the occurrence of the first death. From the same district a large number of human patients were in hospital suffering from toxic cirrhosis of the liver and the pathological changes found in histological sections of liver specimens taken at biopsy or autopsy were indistinguishable from those taken from affected sheep.

Under natural conditions, poisoning of pigs by ragwort must be extremely rare. Harding *et al* (1964) describe their results after feeding *S. jacobaea* to seven pigs over periods from one to three months. The symptoms they exhibited were mainly dyspnoea and fluctuating pyrexia. Post-mortem lesions were mostly in the lungs which were firm, heavy, discoloured and oedematous. Histologically, they showed congestion, haemorrhage, oedema and alveolar epithelialization. The liver and kidneys showed karyomegaly.

As ragwort poisoning takes the form of slow but certain destruction of a vital organ, the liver, recovery is impossible. Unfortunately, no drug is yet known which will halt or even delay the pathological processes involved; the feeding of sugar or molasses has been said to be of benefit during the very early stages of the disease, but any effect is only temporary and is dependent on the state of the liver at the time. Treatment is of no avail after the onset of symptoms and, at best, may do little more than prolong the agony.

Post-mortem examination: by the time an animal dies of ragwort poisoning, plant parts will have passed out of the stomach and bowels, and the poisonous alkaloids will not be found in the tissues in sufficient quantity to make a definite chemical diagnosis. The lesions in the viscera are typical of those which occur when severe liver injury has been followed by cirrhosis.

The characteristic distribution of fibrous tissue in the liver and the fact that the majority of the animals in an exposed group die, are sufficient to warrant a suspicion of ragwort poisoning. Post-mortem findings are hardening and enlargement or shrinking, of the liver; jaundicing of the tissues and fat; dropsical fluid in the abdomen; and at times, effusion of blood into the bowel. In cattle, the gall-bladder is distended and may contain as much as a pint and a half of thick, dark coloured bile. As the result of interference with the flow of blood through the liver, a gelatinous oedema develops along the course of the vessels which flow there from the abdominal viscera; it is particularly noticeable around the vessels on the walls of the stomachs but, should post-mortem examination be delayed, this lesion may disappear. Oedema between the wall and lining membrane of the fourth stomach is fairly constant.

Prevention of poisoning lies in control of the weed in pastures and in crops intended for hay or artificial drying. (When using weedkillers or taking other measures for weed control, it is always advisable for livestock to be kept from treated pastures for a time, as it has long been observed that animals will often eat wilting or newly-dead noxious plants much more readily than if they are growing. Nor is there any valid reason to suppose that ragwort, when killed by a herbicide, is any less toxic than it would have been if cut and included in hay or pulled up by hand and left lying on the ground.)

Common Ragwort, *S. jacobaea*, is one of the injurious weeds specified in the Weeds Act 1959. This Act gives the Ministry of Agriculture, Fisheries and Food, or the local authorities to whom their duties have been delegated, powers to serve notice upon the occupier of any land upon which ragwort is growing, requiring him to take action to prevent the weed from spreading. Failure to comply with such notice renders an occupier liable to prosecution.

For further reading

'DISCUSSION'

K. R. HILL, L. M. MARKSON and R. SCHOENTAL, 1960, *Proc. Roy. Soc. Med.* **53.** 281–8.

LAW CASE

R. S. COCKBURN, *et al*, 1955, *Vet. Rec.* **67.** 640

Cattle

R. ALLCROFT and G. LEWIS (Addendum by K. R. HILL) 1963, *Vet. Rec.* **75.** 487–94.

L. G. DONALD and P. L. SHANKS, 1956, *B. Vet. J.* **112.** 307–11.

R. M. LOOSMORE and L. M. MARKSON, 1961, *Vet. Rec.* **73.** 813–4.

Pigs

J. D. J. HARDING, G. LEWIS, J. T. DONE and R. ALLCROFT, 1964, *Path. Vet.* **1.** 204–20.

Monocotyledons

JUNCAGINACEAE

MARSH ARROW GRASS (*Triglochin palustris* L.), SEA ARROW GRASS (*Triglochin maritima* L.)

Marsh arrow grass is a slender herbaceous perennial with a long thin rhizome. As its name implies, it grows best on wet marshy land, usually among other and taller grasses.

Sea arrow grass is a more robust plant with a shorter and thicker rhizome. It is to be found on salt marshes and near to the sea shores.

Both plants grow in clumps about six to twenty inches high, the leaves are radical and semi-cylindrical, fleshy, dark green and grass-like. Flowers are seen from July to August and are in a close raceme on pedicels which may reach a height of 6 feet (2 m) or more. Fruits, when ripe, are of a golden-brown colour.

Both plants contain cyanogenetic glycosides which vary in amount according to the season and rate of growth. In a dry season, if the soil dries out and the growing plants become stunted, the glycoside content becomes greatly increased. In U.S.A. it is said that from a quarter pound to three pounds of stunted arrow grass taken at one time is sufficient to cause the death of a 600 lb bovine.

For further reading

Farm. Bull. No. 2106. *U.S. Dept. of Agric.*

LILIACEAE

A few species of the Lily family are known to be poisonous and several others are suspect. The growing plants are seldom eaten by animals but the bulbs or roots may be unearthed and, if eaten, cause irritation of the bowels and kidneys. The majority of the leaves, bulbs, and roots contain sufficient acrid juice to prevent animals from eating enough of them to cause death, although they may become ill.

MEADOW SAFFRON, Autumn Crocus (*Colchicum autumnale* L.) (Plate VIII)

Meadow Saffron is a perennial with a corm; the long, dark green, broad, lanceolate leaves are radical and appear in spring. They die down and disappear before the flowers are produced in the autumn. The flowers, closely resembling those of crocus in general appearance, are whitish to pale purple in colour and appear, one or more from each corm, in succession from August to October, dying down very soon after they have opened. The seed vessel remains underground until the following spring, when it appears on the surface in the centre of a cluster of leaves. The bulb-like corms are about the size of a small tulip bulb and lie six to eight inches deep in the soil.

The meadow saffron is seen in meadows in many parts of England, particularly in the south-west and parts of south Wales. It is only seen in Scotland where introduced.

In the past, the plant has been blamed for causing many 'diseases' of animals now known to be due to other causes, and it has been used medicinally for generations as a remedy for gout and rheumatism. It contains two alkaloids, colchicine and colchiceine, both of which are able to withstand drying, storage, and boiling, without loss of their properties. Colchicine is the more toxic of the two.

Because of its power of inhibiting or hindering the division of certain cells of plants and of some animals, colchicine has been used in experimental attempts to produce new variations.

Colchicine is absorbed slowly into the body, and even more slowly eliminated by the kidneys and by the udder in the milk. There is a gradual build-up of the poison in the body and cumulative effects may be seen.

Animals at pasture are likely to eat the leaves in the spring and the flowers in the autumn. Children and calves may be affected by drinking the milk of poisoned cows.

Symptoms shown by cattle are abdominal pain, violent purgation and straining, which may cause eversion of the rectum. Milk and urine may diminish in quantity to the point of total cessation. Weak pulse and coldness, flatulence and gritting of the teeth are common. There is a gradual weakening and loss of muscular power which spreads forward from the hind-quarters. The illness is slow and several days may elapse between the onset of symptoms and death.

Post-mortem examination may reveal seeds or leaves in the stomach during spring, but the flowers are difficult to find in autumn. Acute gastro-enteritis from irritation of the mucous membranes is usually seen; most of the other organs appear to be normal.

First-aid treatment. Demulcents should be given to soothe the irritated bowels and to keep up the patient's resistance until the poison is eliminated. Milk, eggs, sugar, starch gruel and flour gruel, are all indicated stimulants such as strong tea or strong coffee may be added if required.

LILY OF THE VALLEY (*Convallaria majalis* L.)

Lily of the Valley is a perennial with a creeping rootstock. All the leaves are radical, the flowering stems being totally leafless. The bell-shaped white flowers drooping in a loose raceme are, with their sweet fragrance, too well known to require further description.

All parts of the plant contain two glycosides, convallamarin and convallarin. Between them, they are purgative and have an action on the heart somewhat similar to that of digitoxin.

Lily of the Valley is dangerously poisonous if eaten by animals and birds, most of the reports of poisoning by the growing plant being of poultry. The larger animals do not generally have access to it, either in cultivation or in the woodlands of England, where it grows wild.

FRITILLARY, Snake's Head (*Fritillaria meleagris* L.)

Fritillary is one of the prettiest of early spring flowers. It is found wild in the south and south-east of England in water meadows, and is commonly cultivated in gardens all over the country.

The stem is leafy and is about 1 foot high.

The single drooping flower is dull red or yellow on the outside while the inside is lined and spotted and more highly coloured, giving it an appearance like a snake's head.

Fritillary contains an alkaloid, imperialine, which has a poisonous action on the heart.

Actual cases of poisoning by the growing plant have not been recorded within recent years.

BLUEBELL (*Endymion nonscriptus* (L.) Garcke) syns. (*Scilla nonscripta* (L.) Hoffm. and Link; *S. nutans* Sm.)

Bluebells are extremely common in woods and shady places throughout the country, and the blue flowers are much sought after in spring.

The bulbs of bluebells are white and full of a clammy juice.

The leaves are all radical and are generally shorter than the flower stem. They are linear in shape.

The stem is about 1 foot high; on one side it carries a terminal raceme of drooping, bell-like, blue flowers.

Poisoning by bluebells is extremely rare and it is doubtful if animals ever eat the leaves or flowers.

The author saw a hunter poisoned by eating the bulbs which had been thrown into a heap by vandals, who, after despoiling a nearby wood had wrenched them from the flowers and leaves. The horse was seen eating them and was taken away and stabled immediately.

Symptoms were delayed for about six hours, when it was thought by the owner that the animal was choking. There was some abdominal pain and intermittent attempts at vomiting, pulse was slow and weak and the temperature low, the skin was cold and clammy. About ten hours later there was dark-coloured diarrhoea with a considerable amount of blood; urine ceased altogether. The horse was acutely ill for two days, after which he slowly recovered, but passed blood-stained urine for several days.

First-aid treatment. Give demulcents immediately. Eggs, milk, sugar and stimulants are desirable in the early stages. Careful nursing is required during convalescence. Debility and anaemia are very likely sequels.

HYACINTH (*Hyacinthus* spp.)

The bulbs of Hyacinth caused losses from acute purgation, when fed to cattle in Holland during the last war.

BOG ASPHODEL (*Narthecium ossifragum* (L.) Huds.)

The Bog Asphodel is found in bogs and wet moors throughout Britain. It obtained its Latin name 'ossifragum' from the belief of former times that it predisposed to fracture the bones of animals which ate it.

It has a creeping rootstock and a stiff erect stem, from 6 inches to 1 foot in height. The leaves are grass-like and vertically flattened; they sheathe at the base in two opposite ranks like those of the iris. The flowers are bright yellow in colour and are seen in a stiff terminal raceme during summer.

Little definite information has been published concerning the toxicity of the bog asphodel, although it has long had the reputation of being poisonous. Lamont (1952) reports that farmers in Northern Ireland believe it to be a cause of photo-sensitization of sheep. Ender (1955), considers that saponins in bog asphodel are the cause of the liver dysfunction and icterus leading to photo-sensitization of lambs.

For further reading

MEADOW SAFFRON

Cattle

DAVESNE, 1937, *Bull. Soc. vét. prat. Fr.* **21.** 104–9, 127–9, 148–9.

LILY OF THE VALLEY

Fowls

Z. BARDOSI, 1939, *Budapest Thesis.* (Summary in German.)

HYACINTH

Cattle

C. H. NIEUWLAND, 1941, *Tijdschr. Diergeneesk.* **68.** 359–69.

BOG ASPHODEL

Sheep

H. G. LAMONT, 1952, *Rep. Proe. Conf. metab. Dis. B.V.A.* 85.
F. ENDER, 1955, *Nord. Vet. Med.* **7.** 329–77.

GARLIC AND ONION (*Allium* spp.)

The wild species seldom cause illness of animals which eat them, but they are liable to taint both milk and the flesh. Of these, Ramsons (*Allium ursinum* L.) is by far the most common, Crow Garlic (*Allium vineale* L.) and Field Garlic (*Allium oleraceum* L.) have a similar effect.

The cultivated onion has caused poisoning of horses in America; they ate unharvested onions in a field. Out of the nine taken ill seven died. Their breath and urine smelt of onions and their breathing became intensified when forced to move; pulse, temperature and bowels were normal. The mucous membranes of the mouth and conjunctiva were jaundiced and anaemic, and the urine was coffee-coloured.

At post-mortem examination, the subcutaneous tissues were markedly jaundiced and the skeletal muscles were of a salmon pink colour, onion tops and bulbs were found in the stomach. Post-mortem examinations were made of only two of those which died.

Koger (1956), reported from America that cattle died of severe anaemia after eating rotting onions, from which an alkaloid was later isolated which caused immediate death when injected into mice or guinea pigs.

Anaemia has also been seen in poultry which were fed on boiled onions.

Mandelli and Persiani (1964) state that in Italy, four cattle had to be slaughtered out of two hundred which had been fed solely on onions and the survivors, after a change of diet, took two months to recover. Affected animals showed dullness, cessation of rumination, rapid pulse and respiration, blood-stained urine, anaemia and diarrhoea. Some staggered as they walked and others were unable to stand.

Lesions found post-mortem included: inflammation of the alimentary tract, subicteric mucous membranes and large vessels, enlarged spleen, fatty liver and enlarged kidneys with a yellowish-brown colouration of the cortex.

For further reading

F. THORP and G. S. HARSHFIELD, 1939, *J. Amer. vet. med. Ass.* **94.** 52–3.
L. M. KOGER, 1956, *J. Amer. vet. med. Ass.* **129.** 75.
G. MANDELLI and G. PERSIANI, 1964, *Clin. Vet. Milano.* **87.** 1–8.

TRILLIACEAE

HERB PARIS (*Paris quadrifolia* L.)

Herb Paris is a perennial with a creeping rootstock. The stem is simple, 9 inches to 1 foot in height, with a single whorl of four netted-veined, ovate leaves, 2–4 inches long.

The flowers are of a yellowish-green colour, on peduncles 1 or 2 inches above the leaves.

The fruit is a blue-black berry.

Nicholson, in *Lander's Veterinary Toxicology*, says of herb paris: 'All parts of the plant are stated to be toxic and contain a saponin, paristyphnin, which on hydrolysis yields a sugar and an active glycoside, paridin'.

JUNCACEAE

Records of poisoning by rushes are rare in British literature. Poisoning by one species which is not seen in Britain has been described in Australia by Albiston (1937); calves died suddenly after eating *Juncus holoschoenus* R. Br., which was found to contain hydrocyanic acid.

In England, the Hard or Blue rush (*Juncus inflexus* L., syn. *J. glaucus* Sibth.) is responsible for a type of poisoning which is fortunately uncommon. The hard rush is smaller and more wiry than the common rush and of a dark, blue-green colour, the pith is chambered and the panicles of flowers are only 2 or 3 inches below the top. This is the most common species which invades ground where the drainage has been disturbed by mining subsidence in the Midlands.

Cattle do not normally eat hard rushes, except during early spring and late autumn, when hedges and pastures are bare and there is little else. Once they acquire the taste, they gorge upon them and refuse other food. In the early stages there is some mechanical irritation of the stomach and bowels, and diarrhoea is sometimes, but not always, seen. Loss of condition is rapid and the animal becomes nervous and partially blind; the blindness is progressive and after it is complete, there is a series of convulsions which can be brought about by the slightest excitement. Death occurs from cerebral haemorrhage during, or very soon after, a convulsion. There is some similarity between this condition and the convulsions which occur from magnesium deficiency. They differ in that blindness is usually complete before convulsions begin and that injections of magnesium salts do not have the slightest effect in controlling them. Inhalations of small quantities of chloroform, together with subcutaneous injections of brandy and of camphor in ether, are the only medicaments the author has found to be of any value in the treatment of this condition. The animal will usually recover gradually if it can be kept alive for about eight hours.

Recovered animals are nervous for a week or more until their sight returns. They must be housed for a long time afterwards, otherwise, if they return to the same pasture, they gorge on rushes again and repeat the process.

Post-mortem examination reveals rushes in the stomach, usually forming about 90 per cent of the contents. The rumen is normal, the mucous membrane of the leaves of the omasum strips off easily, showing dark red patches of inflammation. The abomasum is intensely inflamed and usually of a fiery red colour. Death occurs from cerebral hæmorrhage, which is found after opening the cranium in the region of the Circle of Willis (circulus arteriosus).

There is no first-aid or simple remedy which might be applied in this condition. In areas where this plant abounds, prevention can be practised by keeping indoors any animals that show nervousness or impaired vision.

For further reading

H. E. Albiston, 1937, *Aust. vet. J.* **13.** 200.

AMARYLLIDACEAE

The Amaryllis family includes the spring-flowering daffodils and snowdrops, so commonly naturalized or wild in woods and fields. They are seldom eaten by animals while growing, but the bulbs when eaten are purgative and emetic. Deaths occurred in Holland during the last war among livestock fed with bulbs in an attempt to augment their diet. The bulbs used were daffodil (*Narcissus*), snowdrops (*Galanthus*), and hyacinth (*Hyacinthus*) (*Liliaceae*).

For further reading

C. H. NIEUWLAND, 1941, *Tijdschr. Diergeneesk.* **68.** 359–69.

IRIDACEAE

The Iris family includes the genera Iris, Gladiolus, and Crocus, many species of which are cultivated in gardens or naturalized in woodlands and semi-wild ornamental places. Only two native wild species of iris are likely to cause poisoning of the domestic animals; they are the Yellow Flag or Yellow Iris and the Stinking Iris or Roast-beef plant. The author has seen a market gardener's horse which recovered from acute colic and diarrhoea, the result of eating the corms of gladioli.

YELLOW FLAG or Yellow Iris (*Iris pseudacorus* L.)

Yellow Flag is found in wet places throughout Britain, in ditches, water-courses, and marshes; it is a perennial with a thick horizontal rootstock which has numerous fibres.

The leaves are light green in colour, stiff and erect and are flattened vertically in one plane. They are in two opposite ranks and at the base form a sheath for the stem. The lower leaves are longer and broader than the upper ones and may be 1–2 inches in breadth and as tall as, or taller than the stem.

The stem stands about 2 feet high and bears two or three large bright yellow flowers at its top. They appear, one at a time, from a large sheathing bract during summer.

The fruit is a green capsule 2–3 inches long which contains numerous pale green to pale brown seeds.

STINKING IRIS, Roast-beef plant, or Gladdon (*Iris foetidissima* L.)

The Stinking Iris is found in woodlands and shady places in the southern counties of England; unless naturalized or introduced, it is seldom seen north of the Midlands.

It is a smaller plant than the yellow flag, with darker green leaves and stem, the flowers are smaller and are violet-blue or whitish-yellow in colour.

The fruit is a capsule which contains numerous bright orange or scarlet seeds.

It receives its name 'stinking iris' from the unpleasant odour which is emitted when the leaves are crushed or bruised.

The irises contain a glycoside, iridin, which withstands drying and storage. Its action on the body is that of a drastic purgative and irritant.

Boddie (1947), records an outbreak of acute diarrhoea in cattle which occurred in the West Highlands of Scotland due to eating the 'roots' of the yellow flag. The affected animals showed acute purgation, and the faeces of some of them contained blood. The temperature rose to between 103°F and 104°F. All of them recovered in a few days. Boddie suggests that hay, containing iris 'roots' and stems, gathered from the marshy ground of the Highlands may account for some of the sudden outbreaks of acute diarrhoea which occur while cattle are housed during winter.

The author saw an outbreak of dysentery in eight pigs which ate the rhizomes of yellow flag after dredging operations for the re-opening of a long-disused canal had brought the rhizomes to the bank. All had bloody diarrhoea, temperatures were subnormal, and two died from exhaustion. The remainder, which were older, recovered, but a sow aborted a few days afterwards.

Iris must be treated with care for although animals seldom eat the growing plants, the rhizomes and leaves are extremely purgative and irritant.

Post-mortem appearances are those of acute gastro-enteritis with effusion of blood into the bowel.

First-aid treatment. Give stimulants and demulcents—eggs, milk, sugar, and flour or starch gruels.

For further reading

G. F. Boddie, 1947, *Vet. Rec.* **59.** 475–6.

DIOSCOREACEAE

BLACK BRYONY (*Tamus communis* L.) (Plate VII)

Black Bryony is the only species of the Yam family native to Britain. The name is liable to cause confusion with white bryony (*Bryonia dioica*), which is botanically a very different plant. For all their differences, they also have much in common from the point of view of their poisonous properties and their general habit.

Black bryony is a common hedge climber in England but is not seen north of the Border. It has a large dark-coloured fleshy rootstock which contains much starch, and long trailing stems often many feet in length.

The leaves are heart-shaped with a tapering point and are on long stalks. They are a shining, bright green in colour which darkens as the fruits ripen in autumn, and are netted with veins between the ribs.

The flowers are unisexual, small and green. The males are in slender racemes, which are often branched and longer than the leaves; the females are in shorter and closer racemes.

The berries are usually very numerous and are bright scarlet when ripe.

Little is known of the active principle of black bryony, but in its action it resembles bryonin, the glycoside of white bryony. Cornevin (1893) and Blackwell (1931) are quoted by Nicholson who says that the leaves are eaten by sheep and goats without ill effects, but the fruit is a narcoto-irritant.

The chief symptoms are vomiting, colic, paralysis of the hind-quarters and rapid death.

Blackwell (1931) records three cases of suspected bryony poisoning in horses, the chief symptoms being sub-acute gastro-enteritis.

According to Cornevin, the root has been used for reducing contusions, and its purgative powers have been long known.

First-aid treatment. Give demulcents—eggs, milk, and sugar, as for other irritant poisons (see page 15).

ARACEAE

CUCKOO-PINT, Wake Robin, Lords and Ladies (*Arum maculatum* L.)

Cuckoo-pint is well known in the English countryside. It is found under hedges, in woods and along the ditches, but it is rare in Scotland. It has a white tuberous rootstock which has an acrid, bitter taste. The leaves are on long, radical stalks and are shaped like an arrowhead; they are dark green and glossy, sometimes spotted with purple or marked with pale, whitish veins. The flower is seen in May or June and consists of a yellowish-green leaf-like spathe from 6–8 inches long which shields the lower half of a purple or (very rarely) yellowish spadix or spike.

The fruits are bright red berries which form on the naked peduncle of the spike, the spathe and leaves having died away before the berries are ripe.

Cuckoo-pint is known to contain an acrid juice which is an acute irritant when applied to the skin. Drying or boiling reduces its activity. Starch extracted from the roots was formerly used for laundry work but was abandoned because of the irritation it caused to the hands of the laundresses. Food preparations from the baked and powdered root were known as Portland arrowroot and Portland sago.

Children are attracted to the berries (which are very poisonous), and pigs have rooted out the tuberous corms. Other livestock seldom touch the plant.

From Italy comes a report that, of seven cows given green fodder containing whole plants of *A. maculatum*, four were unaffected but three developed pulmonary oedema and died in a coma. None of them suffered from diarrhoea.

O'Moore (1955) investigated six outbreaks of *A. maculatum* poisoning in cattle confined in sparse or unpalatable pastures. He found that symptoms were not constant; they included salivation, oedema of the neck, incoordination, convulsions followed by collapse and death. Post-mortem lesions included inflamed mucous membranes of mouth, abomasum and intestines with inflammation of the gall bladder.

First-aid treatment is as for irritant poisons; induce emesis where possible and give demulcents.

For further reading

L. B. O'MOORE, 1955, *Irish Vet. J.* **9.** 146–7.

GRAMINEAE

There are few poisonous species in the very large Grass family. Several are known to contain hydrocyanic acid, but this is present in only such small proportions that it is harmless. Horses are affected by eating some of the cereal grains and of these, wheat, barley, and rye are the most dangerous. Darnel (*Lolium temulentum*) is the only native grass which is likely to cause real harm to both man and animals.

DARNEL, Bearded Darnel (*Lolium temulentum* L.)

Darnel is an annual grass which was formerly a common weed of cornfields. Its poisonous properties have been recognized from ancient times, and writers from the time of Ovid up to the present day have stressed the blindness of people who ate it. It is reputed to be the 'tares' of the Bible, Shakespeare mentions it, and Gerard (1597) remarks that it causes drunkenness in those who eat it in bread hot from the oven. It was at one time used to 'fortify' beer, and in France its inclusion in this beverage was prohibited as long ago as the reign of Saint Louis (1226–1270).

Thanks to our forbears—farmers, millers, and tradesmen alike—this noxious weed has totally disappeared from much of the country, and today there are hundreds of farmers who would not recognize it if they saw it.

In appearance and habit of growth darnel is very like its close cousins, the ryegrasses. It may be distinguished from perennial ryegrass (*Lolium perenne* L.) and Italian ryegrass (*L. multiflorum* Lam., syn. *L. italicum* Braun) by examination of the spikelets. In the spikelet of darnel, the empty outer glume is as long or longer than the spikelet itself, and many of the other glumes have awns which are as long or longer than themselves. In the ryegrasses, the empty outer glume is shorter than the spikelet, and if there are any awns at all, they are shorter than the glumes which bear them.

Only the grain is harmful; the green plant or the threshed-out straw may be eaten by animals with impunity. The poisonous principle is thought to be an alkaloid, temuline, which has been obtained from the seeds. It has been stated by Freeman (1902) that darnel was poisonous only when infected with a fungus, probably *Endoconidium temulentum* Prill. and Delacr., but doubt has been cast upon this by the researches of Steyn (1934). Much more investigation is required before any definite assertions can be made on this question.

Man and the domesticated animals are only liable to be affected when the seeds of darnel become mixed with other grain, and all of them show similar symptoms after eating it. According to Cornevin, symptoms in man and animals are chiefly: vertigo and dizziness, stiffness of the back, slowness in movement, and extreme lassitude. After a good sleep the symptoms may pass off. Should the dose have been large there is, in addition to the above, singing in the ears, nausea and impaired vision, which are followed later by violent abdominal pains, diarrhoea and frequent micturition. If a lethal amount has been taken, all the foregoing symptoms are accentuated and death is preceded by convulsions and delirium.

Urbain and Nouvel (1939) have reported poisoning of captive wild animals by feeding with darnel mixed in oats; reindeer, addax, and gazelle, all showed symptoms which closely conformed to those listed above.

Post-mortem examination of animals which die of darnel poisoning reveals little of note, except perhaps slight enteritis, and possibly congestion of some of the internal organs.

WHEAT (*Triticum* spp.), OATS (*Avena* spp.), BARLEY (*Hordeum vulgare* L.) and RYE (*Secale cereale* L.).

These are the staple cereal foods of the Western races of mankind, by whom they are seldom or never eaten uncooked or without previous preparation by grinding or dressing.

Newer methods of growing, harvesting and storing grain crops, which include the wider use of chemical fertilizers, sprays, combine harvesters, artificial dryers and wet or dry silos, with or without added gases, have largely replaced traditional procedures. While innovations are not necessarily improvements upon what has gone before, there can be little doubt, despite much ill-informed criticism, that the adoption of these adjuncts has greatly minimized the loss of grain and produced a better end-product for the benefit of grower and consumer alike. Consequent upon this, at the present time, larger amounts of home-grown cereals are being used as stockfeed than at any other period in the last half century. And, by no stretch of imagination, can it be said or inferred that the quantity or quality of animals or their products have declined as a result of it.

Up to the moment no toxic substance, specifically produced by a British cereal, has ever been isolated from it. This indicates that any toxicity or serious digestive disturbances occurring among cereal-fed animals is, in the vast majority of instances, the result of feeding upon grain which has been badly harvested or stored, contaminated with chemicals, moulds, ergot or other organisms or of failure, on the part of those responsible for feeding, to recognize the fundamental requirements of herbivorous digestive processes, particularly of those of ruminants. New grain is believed to be less digestible than that which has been stored and, despite modern dryers, there are many owners of valuable horses who will not feed them on oats in the same year that they were harvested.

There is only a remote possibility of oat straw and oat hay becoming poisonous under British conditions of agriculture and climate. In parts of America, deaths among livestock have not been infrequent when fed on oat straw or oat hay grown on certain soils. Under these conditions the plants store large quantities of nitrate of potash (saltpetre, KNO_3) in their stems and leaves; the grain is unaffected. Riggs (1945) in writing of this form of poisoning, states that when oat hay is moistened and exposed to the air, it converts nitrate to nitrite, reaching its maximum content in about twenty hours. The nitrite lessens again after three to five days, and when ten days have elapsed it cannot be detected.

Cracked or coarsely ground wheat is an excellent cattle feed and, in a period between the Wars when large quantities of overseas wheat were being dumped at low prices on the British market, the author, on farms then under his control, fed large numbers of beef cattle on a diet which contained little else beside cracked wheat and hay, without trouble and with excellent end-results. Young pigs, however, when kept on a diet of 60 per cent or more of wheatmeal or bakery waste for about six to eight weeks, commonly showed symptoms of hepatitis and jaundice. Although they recovered clinically after a change of diet, most of them showed liver cirrhosis in varying degree when they came to be slaughtered later.

At the same period, when whole wheat was sold on the markets at a lower price per ton than millers' offals, certain merchants mixed rolled wheat with bran, and wheat meal with sharps. The results were disastrous when horses were fed upon either commodity, although pigs and cattle thrived on them. Bran is the only part of the wheat grain which is safe as an uncooked food for horses. Sharps or middlings and chopped wheat straw are very likely to cause constipation and impaction of the horse's large bowel, and the energy expended by the horse's body in attempting to digest wheat straw is greater than any benefit derived from it.

The power of the grain of wheat, barley and rye, to produce toxic products in the horse's bowel is destroyed by boiling or by soaking until the grain is swollen to its maximum. It is an old custom among waggoners to feed thin horses on boiled or soaked grain in order to fatten them.

Comparatively small amounts of the uncooked grain of wheat, barley, or rye if fed whole or ground into meal, may cause production in the horse's bowel of a histamine-like substance, which is quickly absorbed into the blood-stream. Histamines are products of protein breakdown and, when in concentration in the horse's blood, cause congestion and inflammation of the sensitive laminae or leaves by which the horny hoof is attached to the underlying soft foot. The condition is known by many names—'founder' and 'fever in the feet'—are two of the more everyday ones, and laminitis or equine pododermatitis describes the condition scientifically.

While the grain of barley and rye, particularly when newly harvested, may cause laminitis when fed to the horses of western Europe, between them they form the basis of horses' diets throughout the greater part of northern and eastern Europe and large parts of Asia and North Africa. In the Middle East it is common practice to give horses a course of green barley during spring and barley straw and grain for the rest of the year.

Latterly, barley has become the most widely grown of all cereal crops in Britain and, in addition to by-products from the malting, brewing and distilling trades, larger amounts of cracked barley and barley meal are being used as stockfeed than at any other time in the last half-century. Much of it is consumed in intensive feeding units for the production of 'barley beef'; young tender beef which is in demand. In this type of unit, young cattle are encouraged to eat as much barley as possible at as early age as possible and to be ready for slaughter when between 11 and 13 months old. In the main the system has been highly successful, even though the methods employed differ widely in detail from farm to farm and range from *ad lib.* feeding to carefully controlled individual rationing.

As with every new system of cattle feeding, digestive upsets and other troubles become almost inevitable before a balance between concentrate and roughage has been achieved and heavy barley feeding has proved to be no exception. In fact the position on some of these units is highly reminiscent of what prevailed in the latter half of the third decade of the present century when what were then believed to be revolutionary ideas were being promulgated on the feeding of dairy cows. Then, as now, modifications were necessary and once a balance had been achieved troubles disappeared and the system became standard practice.

The symptoms described by the many authors who have written on illness among barley-fed cattle are in no way specific to barley feeding alone. They can, and do, occur whenever an excessive amount of any cereal or other concentrate forms too high a percentage of the total food intake.

Indigestion, with ruminal stasis and sometimes impaction, is commonly the result of attempting to step up the concentrate content of the diet too rapidly. Similarly, when *ad lib.* feeding is practised, overgorging with dry concentrate by greedy feeders is not uncommon. In these cases, the flora and fauna of the rumen, which live there in a delicately balanced community, become overwhelmed and unable to deal adequately with the ingesta. The first necessity is for ruminal function and fermentation to be restored and, for this, as the rumen contents are almost certain to be acid in reaction, a dose of bakers' yeast will usually suffice. (See page 16).

Harris (1962) describes the rearing and feeding of yarded bullocks upon rations which contained 90 per cent of barley without hay or straw. At slaughter the carcasses graded well but many livers were condemned for necrosis and abscess formation, although few animals showed any indication of these conditions during life. On another farm, he states that 10 out of 90 bullocks, aged from 4 to 6 months, were lost while being fed on the same system. The main feature of these losses was sudden death followed by rapid decomposition of the carcass. Post-mortem appearance of the rumen mucosa suggested hyperkeratosis with clumping of the villi which had small fermenting masses of food and bits of hair trapped between them.

Rix (1966) saw two outbreaks of severe illness from cattle overgorging with meal made from moist-stored barley. This had an odour like 'near-beer' and an alcoholic content. Feeding was *ad lib.* and two cows which kept others away from the trough were surmised to have eaten about fifty pounds of the meal between them. Rix considered that the symptoms were those of acute alcoholic poisoning and they included hepatitis, inappetence, incoordination and staggering gait, slight scouring and polyuria; the urine being frothy. The condition gave cause for anxiety for from four to five days. These symptoms are somewhat reminiscent of those seen in four outbreaks reported by Macdonald *et al.* (1962) in which there was a high mortality rate among younger cattle. Illness began within two days of the commencement of *ad lib.* feeding upon a ration which contained 85 per cent of combine harvested, artificially dried barley which had been harvested about a month previously. After primary dullness and incoordination, affected animals slowly became unresponsive to stimuli and unable to rise. They showed no signs of febrility. Several of those which recovered showed residual blindness and the fatal cases died almost imperceptibly after a period of coma. At post-mortem examination, excessive fluidity of the bowel contents was the only gross abnormality which was seen.

Tympanites, bloat or an excessive accumulation of gas in the rumen is said to be prevalent in some intensive beef units. So much so, in fact, that plastic canulae have been devised to remain permanently in the rumen wall after insertion via the left flank. Gas is almost continually produced by the micro-organisms which inhabit the rumen and so long as there is no oesophageal obstruction and they produce an excess of carbon dioxide (CO_2), it is certain to be eructated without trouble. On the other hand, should the bacterial fermentation be of a type which produces an excess of methane (CH_4), a physiologically inert gas which does not stimulate eructation, the gas is bound to accumulate and may continue to do so until the internal pressure evolved is sufficient to arrest respiration. Methane, which is also known as marsh gas, firedamp, coal gas and natural gas, according to its source, is a highly inflammable hydrocarbon which is derived in the rumen from a bacterial breakdown of carbohydrates. With the right admixture of air it becomes highly explosive so that when tapping off gas from a tympanitic rumen it is very advisable NOT to allow smoking or naked lights in the vicinity.

Before they produce methane in harmful quantities, the responsible organisms require far more critical conditions within the rumen than those organisms upon which normal rumination depends. These conditions include a semi-fluid state of the ingesta and a temperature lower than that of the normal bovine body and, with them in mind, it should not be difficult to envisage how bloat can occur in animals fed indoors on dry but finely divided food and with accesss to a supply of cold water. It is, however, much more likely after the ingestion of an excessive amount of young lush clover or growing corn, particularly if cold and wet with dew or rain.

The results of previous omasitis or inflammation of the third stomach compartment of cattle are not uncommonly discovered during post-mortem examinations. In a survey at the time of slaughter of over 500 unselected cattle, Brownlee and Elliot (1960) found evidence of omasal damage or fenestration of one or more omasal leaves in 15·9 per cent of them. During an attempt to reproduce laminitis in cattle experimentally, in which he allowed 12 steers of 9 to 11½ months of age access to large quantities of coarsely crushed barley, Brownlee (1966) found that by the following day half of them scoured profusely and all of them showed malaise and lost their apetite. One of them became progressively worse and died 7 days later, when the primary lesion found at post-mortem examination was extensive sloughing of several omasal leaves. All the others recovered and none of them showed signs of laminitis. Of the original twelve steers, ten were slaughtered within two months of recovery and, including the one which died, seven of the eleven showed loss of omasal tissue or fenestration of omasal leaves when examined post-mortem (63·6 per cent compared with 15·9 per cent in the earlier survey.)

Laminitis in cattle causes a great deal of pain, lameness and loss of bodily condition. It is the reverse of a disease of poverty and is most commonly seen in well nourished animals to which extra concentrates have been given in order to obtain further improvement. It is seldom or never occasioned by sudden changes in diet and, in most instances, the concentrate increase took place from ten days to a fortnight prior to the exhibition of symptoms. Large numbers of in-calf dairy cows and heifers suffered severely from laminitis during the late 1920s when, already in good condition, they were brought indoors to be subjected to the then fashionable process of being 'steamed-up' i.e., fed almost exclusively on oil-cake prior to calving. Death, as a direct result, was unusual although many were slaughtered for humane reasons after the loss of one or more hooves. The majority of those affected remained chronically lame and, even if no complications occurred at calving, few of them ever produced an economic lactation afterwards.

Maclean (1966) describes the condition as seen in young cattle aged from four and a half to six months, kept intensively in barley beef units. Symptoms were arching of the back, paddling on all four feet and awkwardness of movement. Tapping the feet or squeezing with pincers caused pain and rapid withdrawal. There was local heat and pulsation of the digital artery and affected animals lay down for much of their time. Treatment by anti-histaminics, corticosteroids and bleeding were all unsuccessful. The acute stages subsided to become subacute and all ended in the chronic state with sensitive and even more misshapen feet than those commonly encountered in intensive beef units.

Although there has been much speculation and suggestion as to the probable causes of laminitis in cattle, anything concrete has yet to be published. Whether it can be caused by histamine alone, as in the case of laminitis in horses, is exceedingly doubtful. The numbers of compounds which can be formed within the bovine rumen and their possible combinations, there and elsewhere in the digestive tract, are almost infinite and it may take many years of painstaking research before positive results are obtained.

For further reading

DARNEL

Poultry

R. Fangauf and O. Haensel, 1934, *Landw. Geflügel Ztg.* Aug. 2nd.

Horse

P. Troll, 1941, *Tierärtzl. Rdsch.* **47.** 555–6.

Wild Animals

A. URBAIN and J. NOUVEL, 1939, *Bull. Acad. vét. Fr.* **12.** 77–82.

OAT HAY AND NITRATES

Discovery of Nitrates in Oat Hay

W. B. BRADLEY, H. F. EPPSON and O. A. BEATH, 1938, *J. Amer. vet. med. Ass.* **94.** 541–2.

Poisoning of Livestock

W. B. BRADLEY, H. F. EPPSON and O. A. BEATH, 1940, *Bull. Wyo. agric. Exp. Sta.* **241.**

Treatment with Methylene Blue

W. B. BRADLEY, H. F. EPPSON and O. A. BEATH, 1940, *J. Amer. vet. med. Ass.* **96.** 41–2.

Reduction of Nitrates

O. E. OLSON and A. L. MOXON, 1942, *J. Amer. vet. med. Ass.* **100.** 403–6.

Nitrite Poisoning

C. W. RIGGS, 1945, *Amer. J. vet. Res.* **6.** 194–7.

WHEAT

Cattle

H. E. REDMOND, 1950, *J. Amer. vet. med. Ass.* **117.** 475–6.

BARLEY

Liver Damage. Sudden Death

A. H. HARRIS, 1962, *Vet. Rec.* **74.** 1434.

Mortality with ad lib *feeding*

D. MACDONALD, R. BRADLEY and C. T. MCCREA, 1962, *Vet. Rec.* **74.** 1280.

Alcoholic poisoning

J. C. RIX, 1966, *Vet. Rec.* **78.** 574.

Omasitis

A. BROWNLEE and J. ELLIOT, 1960, *Brit. Vet. J.* **116.** 467–73.
A. BROWNLEE, 1966, *Vet. Rec.* **78.** 606.

Laminitis

C. W. MACLEAN, 1966, *Vet. Rec.* **78.** 223–31.

Plants which Remain Poisonous after Drying and Storage

A LARGE number of plant poisons are stable compounds which are neither changed chemically nor physically by artificial or air drying nor during prolonged storage of plant parts. It is because of this that a very considerable proportion of all animal poisoning occurs during winter, while animals are housed or receiving extra food, as a result of poisonous plant parts having been included in hay, straw, silage or artificially dried or stored crops. This particularly applies to those plants which would be rejected or not eaten in the growing state under normal conditions of grazing. One can instance ragwort which can remain untouched, flourishing and causing no trouble whatsoever in a pasture otherwise grazed bare. Few animals will eat growing ragwort voluntarily, but they may do so after it has been cut, wilted and at least partially dried. Thus it is that the majority of poisoning by such plants as ragwort, horsetail and monkshood can be traced back to hay or other stored fodder.

In long hay or straw there may be some possibility of an animal rejecting unpleasant plant parts but if it has been chaffed or, as often in the case of artificially dried grass, ground into meal and compressed into nuts, rejection becomes more difficult.

A point the author considers worthy of stress is that after a poisonous plant has been killed by the application of a herbicide, what remains of it, up to the moment of total disintegration, has not necessarily lost, nor even reduced, its original toxicity. This, of course, is totally unconnected with any toxic properties the herbicide itself may possess and which, in most instances, will have become relatively harmless long before the plants it has killed have disintegrated. This is in no way intended to decry or discourage the eradication or control of toxic vegetation by chemical means; rather the reverse, but it must be pointed out to stock owners that a risk to animals may still remain from allowing them access to dead plant parts for long after any risk from the herbicide has been eliminated. The gathering together and burning of dead or killed plant remains, with the subsequent burial of the ash, cannot be too strongly advocated. Again, it may not be out of place to point out that cattle, which have licked ash from timber which has, at some time, been dressed with an arsenical preservative, have died from arsenic poisoning.

Plants which contain alkaloids, glycosides, saponins and photo-dynamic substances are among those which most commonly retain their toxicity after drying and storage and a selection from some of those which are known to have caused poisoning in this way is included in the following list.

		Likely to be found in
FUNGI		
Moulds		
Aspergillus flavus		Stored groundnuts, cotton seeds and cereals.
Aspergillus fumigatus		Mouldy hay or grain.
Ergot		
Claviceps purpurea		Grain, possibly hay.
PTERIDOPHYTA		
Equisetaceae		
Equisetum spp.	Horsetails	Chiefly hay and straw.
Polypodiaceae		
Pteridium aquilinum	Bracken	Hay, as bedding or packing material.
GYMNOSPERMAE		
Taxaceae		
Taxus baccata	Yew	Clippings, discarded decorations, wreaths and garden refuse heaps.
ANGIOSPERMAE		
Ranunculaceae		
Helleborus spp.	Hellebores	Hay, brushings and garden refuse.
Aquilegia spp.	Columbine	Hay or grass cut from woodlands, garden refuse.
Aconitum spp.	Monkshood	Brushings from stream and hedge banks, road verges and garden refuse.
Delphinium spp.	Larkspur	Straw and garden refuse.

Papaveraceae		
Papaver spp.	Poppy	Residues from seed crushing.
Chelidonium majus	Greater Celandine	Garden refuse and brushings.
Hypericaceae		
Hypericum spp.	St. John's Wort	Hay and hedge bank brushings.
Caryophyllaceae		
Agrostemma githago	Corn Cockle	Seeds in grain, stems in straw.
Saponaria officinalis	Crow Soap	Hay, brushings from banks and ditches.
Arenaria spp.	Sandworts	Hay or close cropped mowings.
Stellaria spp.	Chickweed	In brushings from cultivated land and garden refuse.
Linaceae		
Linum usitatissimum	Flax	Seeds and in cake (Cyanogenetic glycoside and goitrogen).
Rhamnaceae		
Rhamnus catharticus	Purging Buckthorn	Bark and twigs in brushings and trimmings.
Frangula alnus	Alder Buckthorn	Bark and twigs in brushings and trimmings.
Papilionaceae		
Lupinus spp.	Lupin	Lupin hay, garden refuse.
Laburnum anagyroides	Laburnum	Leaves, seeds, bark and roots.
Umbelliferae		
Cicuta virosa	Cowbane	Stems and leaves in brushings from around ditches and streams. Roots on surface after ditching.
Oenanthe crocata	Water Dropwort	
Cucurbitaceae		
Bryonia dioica	Bryony	Stems in hay and hedge brushings, roots on surface after ditching.
Cannabiaceae		
Cannabis sativa	Hemp	Hay from roadsides and places where wild birds have been fed.
Ericaceae		
Rhododendron spp.		Garden refuse and shrubbery trimmings.
Primulaceae		
Cyclamen spp.	Sowbread	Dried grass, close mowings and short straw.
Anagallis spp.	Pimpernel	
Solanaceae		
Datura spp.	Thornapple	Hay from near hedge banks and around old buildings.
Hyoscyamus niger	Henbane	
Atropa bella-donna	Deadly Nightshade	
Solanum nigrum	Black Nightshade	Hay and dried grass, particularly from newly sown leys. Among peas grown for processing.
Solanum tuberosum	Potato	Tubers badly stored and exposed to light.
Scrophulariaceae		
Digitalis purpurea	Foxglove	Hay and brushings.
Compositae		
Senecio spp.	Ragworts	Hay, dried grass, silage.

MONOCOTYLEDONS		
Liliaceae		
Convallaria majalis	Lily of the Valley	Garden refuse, brushings from shaded banks and woodlands.
Fritillaria meleagris	Fritillary	Hay (early).
Colchicum autumnale	Meadow Saffron	Hay (late).
Trilliaceae		
Paris quadrifolia	Herb Paris	Hay from damp places.
Iridaceae		
Iris spp.	Iris	Hay from damp places, rhizomes on surface after ditching or excavation.
Dioscoriaceae		
Tamus communis	Black Bryony	Stems in hay from hedge banks. tubers on surface after ditching.
Graminae		
Lolium temulentum	Darnel	Seeds mixed in grain.
Triticum aestivum	Wheat	New grain (before Christmas).
Hordeum vulgare	Barley	New grain (before Christmas).
Secale cereale	Rye	New grain (before Christmas).

Plants which Affect Milk

THERE are many plants, some of them poisonous, which if eaten by lactating cows, cause alterations in the secretion, odour, taste, or physical characteristics of their milk. The poisonous principles of a few of these plants are secreted by the udder in sufficient quantities to render the milk poisonous for children and calves, but in the vast majority of instances, the odour or taste is so repulsive that it is not drunk voluntarily by either. Many of the most unpleasant taints are harmless; milk tainted by garlic or onion, for instance, would have to be taken in much larger quantities than those normally consumed if it is to be the cause of gastric disturbance. Tainted milk is a nuisance; it is unpleasant for the consumer and an expense to the dairyman. The milk from poisoned animals or those sick from other causes, particularly if they are receiving medicines, should be kept apart until it has been ascertained that it is not tainted and is safe for use. The milk of a cow which is suffering from acorn or bracken poisoning, although the quantity may be reduced, is usually sufficiently bitter to taint a whole churn of good milk and render it unsaleable. Where the milk is tainted by plants it is extremely likely that the flesh is also tainted, and for this reason many carcasses of poisoned animals are valueless after they have been slaughtered in an emergency, even though the appearance is good and the poisonous principles have been rendered harmless.

Milk products are also affected by some plants; wood sorrel, for instance, has been blamed for centuries by dairymaids when butter would not churn, and cheesemakers go to no end of trouble to get rid of the wild mints which prevent the formation of curd. For the convenience of readers in attempting to trace trouble, some of the plants which are known to affect milk, and the conditions they cause, have been listed in tabular form.

	Reduces milk secretion	Taints of taste and odour	Bitter milk	Effect on butter and cheese	Change of colour	Stringy milk
Anemone spp.		*				
Bog Asphodel (*Narthecium ossifragum*) .						
Bracken (*Pteridium aquilinum*) . .	*		*	Bitter butter and cheese		
Buckthorn (*Rhamnus* spp.) . . .	*					
Buttercups (*Ranunculus* spp.). . .	*		*	yellow butter, bitter flavour	yellow-ish red	
Butterwort (*Pinguicula vulgaris*) . .		*		disagreeable taste to both		*
Chamomiles (*Anthemis* spp. and *Matricaria* spp.)	*	*				
Cowbane (*Cicuta virosa*) . . .	*					
Cow-wheat (*Melampyrum* spp.) . .			*			
Fools' Parsley (*Aethusa cynapium*) . .		*				
Garlics and Onions (*Allium* spp.) . .		*		unpleasant butter		
Hedge Mustard (*Sisymbrium officinale*) .		*				
Hellebores (*Helleborus* spp.) . . .				unpleasant butter and cheese		
Hemlock (*Conium maculatum*) . .	*	*				
Henbane (*Hyoscyamus niger*) . . .	*	*				
Horsetails (*Equisetum* spp.) . . .	*	*		cream and butter unpleasant		
Ivy (*Hedera helix*)	*	*				
Knotgrass, Knotweed (*Polygonum aviculare*)			*			
Laburnum	*		*			
Lesser Sium (*Sium erectum*) . . .		*				
Lesser Wartcress (*Coronopus didymus*) .		*				
Marsh Marigold (*Caltha palustris*) . .	*		*	bitter milk and butter		
Meadow Saffron (*Colchicum autumnale*) .	*					
Mercury; Annual and Dog's (*Mercurialis* spp.)	*				bluish	

	Reduces milk secretion	Taints of taste and odour	Bitter milk	Effect on butter and cheese	Change of colour	Stringy milk
Mints (*Mentha* spp.)		*		prevents clotting		
Monkshood (*Aconitum napellus*)	*					
Oak; leaves and acorns (*Quercus* spp.)	*		*	cheese affected on keeping		
Ox-eye daisy (*Chrysanthemum* spp.)		*		tainted butter		
Pennycress (*Thlaspi arvense*)		*				
Pepper Saxifrage (*Silaum silaus*)		*				
Potatoes, green (*Solanum*)	*	*				
Rhododendron spp.	*		*		red	
Sages (*Salvia* spp.)		*				
St. John's Wort (*Hypericum* spp.)	*					
Sorrel and Sheep's Sorrel (*Rumex* spp.)	*			difficulty in churning and clotting		
Spurges (*Euphorbia* spp.)				sharp taste in butter		
Sugar beet pulp		*				
Sugar beet tops	*	*		difficulty in churning and clotting		
Tansy (*Tanacetum vulgare*)		*		unpleasant milk and butter		
Tormentil (*Potentilla erecta*)						*
Turnips (*Brassica* spp.)		*		unpleasant milk and butter		
Water Parsnip (*Sium latifolium*)		*		unpleasant milk and butter		
Wild Radish (*Raphanus raphanistrum*)	*	*				
Wood Sorrels (*Oxalis* spp.)		*		difficulty in churning		
Wormwood (*Artemisia absinthium*)		*				
Yarrow (*Achillea millefolium*)			*	bitter butter		
Yew (*Taxus baccata*)	*	*				

Glossary

(*med.*= medical; vet.= veterinary; *bot.*= botanical)

Abomasum (*vet.*): the fourth, or rennet stomach of ruminants.

Abortion (*vet. med.*): the premature birth of young.

Abortifacient (*vet. med.*): a substance which, if taken internally, may cause abortion.

Acetonaemia (*vet*): a disease of animals in which acetone bodies or ketones are present in the blood stream.

Alimentary tract (*med. vet.*): the digestive tract, from mouth to anus.

Alkaloid (*med. vet. bot.*): a basic chemical substance, often poisonous, derived from plants.

Anaemia (*med. vet.*): a deficiency of red corpuscles in the blood or of blood itself.

Annual (*bot.*): a plant which grows from seed, flowers, and dies within a year.

Antidote (*med. vet.*): a substance or medicine given to neutralize or prevent the effects of a poison.

Asphyxia (*med. vet.*): stoppage of breathing, suffocation.

Astringent (*med. vet.*): a medicine given to allay diarrhoea.

Awn (*bot.*): a bristle or hair-like appendage to a fruit or to a glume, as in barley and some other grasses.

Biennial (*bot.*): a plant which flowers and dies in the second year after growing from seed.

Bisexual (*bot.*): a flower which is both male and female.

Blanching (*vet. med.*): pallor of mucous membranes and skin.

Blastogenesis (*med. vet.*): a condition in which such cells as white blood corpuscles, which are normally separate, remain together in groups or clumps instead of separating after mitosis or cell-division has occurred several times.

Botulism (*med. vet.*): a bacterial disease.

Bract (*bot.*): a modified leaf, usually placed singly beneath each pedicel.

Calyx (*bot.*): outer part of the perianth of a flower consisting typically of a whorl of green sepals.

Campanulate (*bot.*): bell-like.

Capsule (*bot.*): a dry fruit, which usually opens at valves, slits or pores to set free seeds when ripe.

Carcinogen (*med. vet.*): a substance which is capable of causing cancer.

Carpel (*bot.*): part of the (female) pistil of a flower, consisting of stigma, style and ovary.

Cerebral (*med. vet.*): relating to the cerebrum, the largest part of the brain.

Coma (*med. vet.*): profound unconsciousness from which the patient cannot be roused.

Congestion (*med. vet.*): the presence of an abnormal amount of blood in an organ or part.

Conjunctiva (*med. vet.*): the thin lining membrane of the eyelids which also covers the eyeball.

Conjunctivitis (*med. vet.*): inflammation of the conjunctiva.

Contusions (*med. vet.*): bruises.

Convulsant (*med. vet.*): a poison which causes convulsions.

Convulsion (*med. vet.*): a violent involuntary contraction of muscles.

Corm (*bot.*): underground bulbous root.

Corolla (*bot.*): inner part of the perianth of a flower; typically a whorl of coloured petals.

Corymb (*bot.*): a flower cluster in which the flower stalks, although they arise from different places on the stem and are of different lengths, give the cluster a level flat appearance at the top.

Cranium (*med. vet.*): the bony part of the skull which contains the brain.

Crenate (*bot.*): of leaves, the edges of which are scalloped or notched.

Cyme (*bot.*): similar to a panicle except that the upper flowers open first and the lower ones later.

Detoxicate: to render a poison harmless.

Deciduous plants (*bot.*): those which shed all their leaves annually.

Decumbent stems (*bot.*): stems which spread horizontally and later turn upwards and become erect.

Defaecation (*med. vet.*): the passage of faeces, dunging.

Delirium (*med.*): disordered state of mind with great excitement, and often hallucinations.

Diarrhoea (*med. vet.*): scouring, the passage of liquid faeces.

Digit (*med. vet.*): a finger or toe, a claw or hoof in animals.

Digitate leaves (*bot.*): those in which several leaflets diverge from one point, like the fingers of a hand.

Dilation (*med. vet.*): opening wide, usually the pupil of the eye or nostrils.

Dioecious plants (*bot*): those in which the male and female flowers appear on separate plants.

Distension (*med. vet.*): the filling of a hollow organ to more than its usual capacity.

Diuresis (*med. vet.*): excessive urination.

Dysentery (*med. vet.*): an illness characterized by diarrhoea with blood and mucus in the faeces.

Emaciation (*med. vet.*): wasting of the body, excessive thinness due to disease.

Emesis (*med. vet.*): vomiting.

Emetic (*med. vet.*): a substance or medicine given to cause vomiting.

Emmenagogue (*med.*): a substance prescribed to increase menstrual flow.

Emphysema (*med. vet.*): air or gas in the interstices of a tissue.

Enema, *pl.* enemata (*med. vet.*): clyster, rectal injection.

Enteritis (*med. vet.*): inflammation of the bowels.

Enzyme (*bot.*): a ferment.

Extremities (*med. vet.*): the extreme parts of the body, i.e., feet, hands, ears, horns, and tail.

Faeces (*med. vet.*): stools, dung.

Flora: the plant population of a region; also used of micro-organisms in the rumen, bowels, etc.

Foetid (*med. vet. bot.*): maladorous, stinking.

Friable: easily crumbled.

Gangrene (*med. vet.*): necrosis of a part of the body, often with decomposition or shrivelling up.

Genetics (*med. vet. bot.*): the study of heredity and breeding.

Genus, *pl.* genera (*bot.*): the smallest natural group containing distinct species and given a common name, e.g., *Allium*, shared by the included species, e.g., *Allium ursinum*, *A. vineale*, etc.

Glabrous (*bot.*): without hairs of any kind.

Glaucous (*bot.*): of a pale bluish-green colour, often coloured with a fine waxy bloom.

Globular (*bot.*): shaped like a small globe.

Glumes (*bot.*): bracts which enclose the flowers of the sedges and grasses.

Glycoside (*bot. chem.*): a substance found in plants which breaks down into sugar and a poison on fermentation.

Goitrogen (*med. vet.*): a substance which affects thyroid function or causes goitre.

Granules: small grains.

Haematuria (*med. vet.*): urine which contains blood.

Haemoglobin (*med. vet.*): the red colouring matter of blood.

Haemoglobinuria (*med. vet.*): urine which contains haemoglobin.

Haemolysis (*med. vet.*): breakdown of the red blood corpuscles.

Haemolytic (*med. vet*): a substance which causes haemolysis.

Haemorrhage (*med. vet.*): bleeding, a flow of blood.

Hallucinations (*med.*): illusions, seeing things which are not present.

Hepatitis (*med. vet.*): inflammation of the tissue of the liver.

Hepatotoxic (*med. vet.*): poisonous to liver cells.

Herbaceous perennials (*bot.*): plants in which the greater part dies after flowering, leaving only the rootstock to produce next year's growth.

Indigenous: native of the country in which it was produced.

Involucre (*bot.*): a whorl of bracts around an inflorescence (flower cluster).

Jaundice (*med. vet.*): The Yellows, a disease in which bile pigments appear to stain skin and mucous membranes yellow.

Lactation: the production of milk.

Laminitis (*vet.*): fever in the feet, founder, inflammation of the sensitive laminae in hoof-bearing animals.

Lanceolate leaves (*bot.*): shaped like a spearhead, tapering to each end.

Lesion (*med. vet.*): an individual patch of disease in a tissue.

Linear leaves (*bot.*): those which are long and narrow.

Lymph nodes (*med. vet.*): small lymphatic glands.

Mesenteric (*med. vet.*): relating to the mesentary, a fold of peritoneum which attaches intestines to the abdominal wall.

Micturition: the passage of urine.

Monoecious (*bot.*): when male and female flowers are separate, but on the same plant.

Mucous membrane (*med. vet.*): lining membrane of respiratory, alimentary, and urogenital tracts.

Mucus (*med. vet.*): slimy substances secreted by mucous membrane.

Narcosis (*med. vet.*): sleep or stupor induced by a drug or poison (narcotic).

Nauseous—sickly.

Necrosis (*med. vet.*): death of part of a tissue.

Node (*bot.*): knob on root or branch, joint where leaves are borne on stem.

Nodule (*med. vet.*): a small round lump.

Noxious: harmful, unwholesome, poisonous.

Oedema (*med. vet.*): dropsy of a tissue.

Omasum (*vet.*): the third compartment or "Bible" of the stomach of ruminants.

Ovate (*bot.*): egg-shaped outline, usually relating to leaves.

Ovoid (*bot.*): egg-shaped, solid, usually relating to fruit.

Panacea: a cure-all.

Panicle (*bot.*): a loose flower cluster in which the lower ones open first, and the axis is divided into branches each with two or more flowers.

Paroxysm (*med. vet.*): a spasm, sudden onset of symptoms especially if recurrent.

Pathological (*met. vet.*): diseased.

Pedicel (*bot.*): an ultimate flower-stalk supporting a single flower.

Peduncle (*bot.*): the stalk of a flower, or of an inflorescence.

Perennial (*bot.*): see herbaceous perennial.

Peritoneum (*med. vet.*): the shiny lining membrane of the abdominal cavity which also covers the organs it contains.

Petechiae (*med. vet.*): small bleeding points in an organ or tissue.

Petiole (*bot.*): leaf-stalk.

Phytohaemagglutinin (*med. vet.*): a substance of plant origin which is capable of causing already separate blood cells to clump together.

Phytomitogen (*med. vet.*): a substance of plant origin which initiates mitosis or cell-division when introduced to an animal body.

Pinnate (*bot.*): feathery leaves, when the leaflets are numerous on either side of a midrib.

Prolapse (*med. vet.*): the falling down of an organ, which may extrude through a natural orifice.

Purgative (*med. vet.*): a strongly laxative medicine, a substance which causes purging.

Raceme (*bot.*): flowers borne on pedicels along a simple stem or rachis.

Radical leaves (*bot.*): leaves which arise from a rhizome or from the base of the stem.

Radicle (*bot.*): the first root of the embryo or young seedling.

Reticulum (*vet.*): the second compartment, or "honeycomb", of the stomachs of ruminants.

Rumen (*vet.*): the first compartment or "paunch", of the stomachs of ruminants.

Rumenotomy (*vet.*): an operation for opening the rumen via the animal's left flank.

Ruminant (*vet.*): an animal which chews its cud; cattle, sheep, goats, deer, etc.

Ruminate (*vet.*): to chew the cud.

Samara (*bot.*): a winged fruit, as "keys" of ash, or fruits of sycamore.

Sclerosis (*med. vet.*): hardening of a tissue, e.g., liver, or blood vessels.

Sedative (*med. vet.*): a calming or quietening medicine.

Sepal (*bot.*): a part of the calyx of a flower.

Serrated (*bot.*): of leaves, notched at the edge like the teeth of a saw.

Slough (*med. vet.*): dead tissue which drops away from living flesh.

Spadix (*bot.*): a flower-spike with a fleshy axis.

Spatulate (*bot.*): spoon-shaped or racket-shaped.

Species(*bot.*): a unit of classification subordinate to a "genus", superior to a "variety".

spp.: abbreviation of species (pl.).

Spikelets (*bot.*): in grasses, the flower-head unit composed of two glumes and one or more flowers.

Stamen (*bot.*): male organ of flowering plant.

Stellate (*bot.*): leaves, etc., arranged in a whorl like a star.

Subcutaneous (*med. vet.*): under the skin.

Syndrome (*med. vet.*): a number of symptoms which taken together reveal the normal picture of a disease.

syn.: this abbreviation (of synonym) indicates that the name which follows is no longer used, the name before it being now accepted as correct.

Torpid (*med. vet.*): inactive, sluggish.

Toxic (*med. vet. bot.*): poisonous.

Trifoliate (*bot.*): a leaf with three leaflets as clover, laburnum, etc.

Tympanitic (*med. vet.*): distended with gas.

Ubiquitous: everywhere.

Umbel (*bot.*): a flower cluster in which all stalks or rays spring from a common centre like the ribs of an umbrella forming a flat or convex surface.

Unisexual (*bot.*): single sexed. When all flowers on a plant are of one sex.

Volatile: a substance which evaporates rapidly.

Volva (*bot.*): the outer veil of certain of the larger fungi, particularly *Amanita,* which covers the whole fungus when young, but breaks during growth, leaving signs of its presence in the cup at the base of the stem of Death Cap, and the white patches on the cap of Fly Agaric, etc.

Whorl (*bot*): a ring of leaves, etc., around a stem.

Index

Printed in England for Her Majesty's Stationery Office
by Colibri Press Ltd. London Dd290068 K16 2/76